SADLIER

VOCABULARY WORKSHOP®

ENRICHED EDITION

Level E

Jerome Shostak

Senior Series Consultant

Vicki A. Jacobs, Ed.D.
Associate Director, Teacher Education Program
Lecturer on Education
Harvard Graduate School of Education
Cambridge, Massachusetts

Series Consultants

Louis P. De Angelo, Ed.D.
Associate Superintendent
Diocese of Wilmington
Wilmington, Delaware

Sarah Ressler Wright, NBCT
English Department Chair
Rutherford B. Hayes High School
Delaware City Schools, Ohio

John Heath, Ph.D.
Professor of Classics
Santa Clara University
Santa Clara, California

Carolyn E. Waters, JD, Ed.S.
ELA/Literacy 6–12 Supervisor
Cobb County School District
Marietta, Georgia

Sadlier

Reviewers

The publisher wishes to thank for their comments and suggestions the following teachers and administrators, who read portions of the series prior to publication.

Cover: Concept/Art and Design: MK Advertising and William H. Sadlier, Inc.; Cover pencil: Shutterstock/VikaSuh. **Photo Credits:** Interior: akg-images: 51 *top*, 109 *top*; RIA Nowosti: 184 *top*. Alamy: 12 *right*, 31; AF Archive: 97; Alistair Heap: 98 *top inset*; Archive Images: 60 *top*; Dinodia Photos: 179; Geraint Lewis: 13 *inset*, 169; Image Source: 33 *center*; Ivy Close Images : 65; Jill Hunter: 146; Jochen Tack: 32 *top*; Mark Boulton: 22 *inset l.*; MARKA: 27; Mary Evans Picture Library: 23 *inset*, 88 *top*; Mary Evans Picture Library: 12 *right*; Photos 12: 126 *right*; Trinity Mirror/Mirrorpix: 88 *bottom*. Art Resource, NY: 17; bpk, Berlin/Staatliche Antikensammlung/Alfredo dagli Orti: 151; DeA Picture Library: 174 *background*; Mingei International Museum: 147 *center*; Nick Saunders/Barbara Heller Photo Library, London: 147 *bottom*; Nimatallah: 174 *left*; Réunion des Musées Nationaux: 50 *top inset*; Scala: 50 *bottom*; Scala/White Images: 61 *top*, 164 *left*; The New York Public Library: 37. Artbeats: 22 frame. Associated Press: 70 *inset*, 71 *left*. The Bridgeman Art Library: 164 *background*; Ken Welsh: 12 *left*; The Stapleton Collection: 22 *right*. Corbis/Bettmann: 69, 89 *background*, 93, 103; Chris Hellier: 189; Digital Stock: 13 *background*; Heritage Images: 173; Hulton-Deutsch Collection: 183; Julie Lemberger: 136 *right*; PoodlesRock: 141; The Gallery Collection: 23 *top*. Everett Collection: 59, 75, 79, 145, 155; 20th Century Fox Film Corp.: 107, 117; ITV/Rex Features: 193. Getty Images: 98 *left*; Congressional Quarterly: 137 *top*; DEA/G. DAGLI ORTI: 108 *top*; Petr Svarc: 109 *bottom*; The Bridgeman Art Library: 108 *bottom*. The Granger Collection, New York: 41. The Image Works/James Marshal: 99 *bottom*; Lebrecht: 184 *bottom*; Museum of London/HIP: 89 *inset*. The Kobal Collection/20th Century Fox: 135. Lebrecht Music & Arts: 113, 185 *top*. Mary Evans Picture Library: 60 *bottom*; Classic Stock/C.P. Cushing: 131; Ronald Grant Archive: 21. Masterfile/Imagebroker: 71 *right*. Photo Edit/Michelle D. Bridwell: 137 *bottom*. Photo Researchers, Inc./Biology Pics: 175; John Eastcott & Yva Momatiuk: 55; Patrick Landmann: 32 *bottom*. Photodisc: 50 frame, 99 *inset*, 126 *background*, 126 frame, 126, 127, 136 *background*, 137 *background*, 164. Pierre Gildesgame Maccabi Sports Museum, Ramat-Gan, Israel: 126 *center*. Punchstock/Photodisc: 13 frame. Shutterstock: Booka: 33 *top*; Fedorov Oleksiy: 60 wreath, 61 wreath; Ice-Storm: 88 paper; Janika: 98 *background*; Kaspars Grinvalds: 99 frame; MustafaNC: 88 frame; Myotis: 33 *bottom*; nadi555: 126 frame; NASA: 147 *top right*; Olena Zaskochenko: 70 frame; Saranai: 50 *bottom center*, 51 scroll; VikaSuh: 1; zhu difeng: 22 *background*. Sport Club Hakoah, Vienna: 126 *left*, 127 *inset*. Wikipedia: 147 *top*.

Illustration Credits: Tim Haggerty: 46, 84, 122, 160, 198.

 and **VOCABULARY WORKSHOP®** are registered trademarks of William H. Sadlier, Inc.

Printed in the United States of America.
ISBN: 978-0-8215-8010-3
12 13 BRR 22 21 20

For additional online resources, go to vocabularyworkshop.com and enter the Student Access Code: VW12SDY4F9RB

ENRICHED EDITION: New Features

For more than five decades, VOCABULARY WORKSHOP has proven to be a highly successful tool for guiding systematic vocabulary growth and developing vocabulary skills. It has also been shown to help students prepare for standardized tests.

New in this edition are the **Reading Passages, Writing, Vocabulary in Context,** and **Word Study** activities. Nonfiction, high-interest passages use 15 or more of the Unit vocabulary words in context. Two writing prompts require a response to the reading and provide practice in writing for standardized tests. New Vocabulary in Context activities present words from the Unit as they are used in classic works of literature. After every three units, Word Study activities, developed in conjunction with Common Core State Standards requirements, provide practice with idioms, adages, and proverbs, as well as denotation and connotation and classical roots.

Look for the new **QR** (Quick Response) codes on the **Reading Passage** and **Vocabulary in Context** pages. The code can be read with a smartphone camera. To read the QR code, download any free QR code application to a smartphone. Snap the code with a smartphone camera to go directly to iWords for the Unit or an interactive quiz. With iWords you can listen to one word at a time or download all of the words in a Unit to listen to them at your convenience.

The new structure of VOCABULARY WORKSHOP is made up of 15 Units. Each Unit consists of the following sections: a **Reading Passage, Definitions, Choosing the Right Word, Synonyms and Antonyms, Completing the Sentence, Writing,** and **Vocabulary in Context**. Together, these exercises provide multiple and varied exposures to the taught words—an approach consistent with and supportive of research-based findings in vocabulary instruction.

Five **Reviews** cover Vocabulary for Comprehension and Two-Word Completions. Vocabulary for Comprehension is modeled on the reading sections of standardized tests, and as in those tests, it presents reading comprehension questions, including specific vocabulary-related ones, that are based on a reading passage.

A **Final Mastery Test** assesses a selection of words from the year with activities on Synonyms, Antonyms, Analogies, Two-Word Completions, Supplying Words in Context, Word Associations, and Choosing the Right Meaning.

In each level of VOCABULARY WORKSHOP, 300 key words are taught. The words have been selected according to the following criteria: currency and general usefulness; frequency of appearance on recognized vocabulary lists; applicability to, and appearance on, standardized tests; and current grade-level research.

ONLINE COMPONENTS
vocabularyworkshop.com

At **vocabularyworkshop.com** you will find iWords, an audio program that provides pronunciations, definitions, and examples of usage for all of the key words presented in this level of VOCABULARY WORKSHOP. You can listen to one word at a time or, if you wish, download to an MP3 player all of the words of any given Unit. You will then be able to listen to the audio program for that Unit at your convenience.

At **vocabularyworkshop.com** you will also find **interactive vocabulary quizzes, flashcards, games and puzzles** that will help reinforce and enrich your understanding of the key words in this level of VOCABULARY WORKSHOP.

CONTENTS

iWords Audio Program available at **vocabularyworkshop.com**.

VOCABULARY STRATEGY: Using Context

The **context** of a word is the printed text of which that word is part. By studying the word's context, we may find **clues** to its meaning. We might find a clue in the immediate or adjoining sentence or phrase in which the word appears; in the topic or subject matter of the passage; or in the physical features—such as photographs, illustrations, charts, graphs, captions and headings—of a page itself.

The **Vocabulary in Context**, **Vocabulary for Comprehension**, and **Choosing the Right Meaning** exercises that appear in the Units, the Reviews, and Final Mastery Test provide practice in using context to decode unfamiliar words.

Three types of context clues appear in the exercises in this book.

A **restatement clue** consists of a *synonym* for or a *definition* of the missing word. For example:

Faithfully reading a weekly newsmagazine not only broadens my knowledge of current events and world or national affairs but also _____ my vocabulary.

a. decreases   **b.** fragments   **c.** increases   **d.** contains

In this sentence, *broadens* is a synonym of the missing word, *increases*, and acts as a restatement clue for it.

A **contrast clue** consists of an *antonym* for or a phrase that means the opposite of the missing word. For example:

"My view of the situation may be far too rosy," I admitted.
"On the other hand, yours may be a bit (**optimistic, bleak**)."

In this sentence, *rosy* is an antonym of the missing word, *bleak*. This is confirmed by the presence of the phrase *on the other hand*, which indicates that the answer must be the opposite of *rosy*.

An **inference clue** implies but does not directly state the meaning of the missing word or words. For example:

"A treat for all ages," the review read, "this wonderful novel combines the _____ of a scholar with the skill and artistry of an expert _____."

a. ignorance . . . painter   **c.** wealth . . . surgeon
b. wisdom . . . beginner   **d.** knowledge . . . storyteller

In this sentence, there are several inference clues: (a) the word *scholar* suggests *knowledge*; (b) the words *novel*, *artistry*, and *skill* suggest the word *storyteller*. These words are inference clues because they suggest or imply, but do not directly state, the missing word or words.

VOCABULARY STRATEGY: Word Structure

Prefixes, **suffixes**, and **roots**, or **bases**, are word parts. One strategy for determining an unknown word's meaning is to "take apart" the word and think about the parts. Study the prefixes and suffixes below to help you find out the meanings of words in which they appear

Prefix	Meaning	Sample Words
com-, con-	together, with	compatriot, contact
de-, dis-	lower, opposite	devalue, disloyal
il-, im-, in-, ir, non-, un-	not	illegal, impossible, inactive, irregular, nonsense, unable
super-	above, greater than	superimpose, superstar

Noun Suffix	Meaning	Sample Nouns
-acy, -ance, -ence, -hood, -ity, -ment, -ness, -ship	state, quality, or condition of, act or process of	adequacy, attendance, persistence, neighborhood, activity, judgment, brightness, friendship
-ant, -eer, -ent, -er, -ian, -ier, -ist, -or	one who does or makes something	contestant, auctioneer, resident, banker, comedian, financier, dentist, doctor
-ation, -ition, -ion	act or result of	organization, imposition, election

Verb Suffix	Meaning	Sample Verbs
-ate	to become, produce, or treat	validate, salivate, chlorinate
-fy, -ify, -ize	to cause, make	liquefy, glorify, legalize

Adjective Suffix	Meaning	Sample Adjectives
-al, -ic,	relating to, characteristic of	natural, romantic
-ful, -ive, -ous	full of, given to, marked by	beautiful, protective, poisonous

A **base** or **root** is the main part of a word to which prefixes and suffixes may be added. On the Classical Roots page of the Word Study section, you will learn more about Latin and Greek roots and the English words that derive from them. The following lists may help you figure out the meaning of new or unfamiliar words.

Greek Root	Meaning	Sample Words
-cryph-, -crypt-	hidden, secret	apocryphal, cryptographer
-dem-, -demo-	people	epidemic, democracy
-gen-	race, kind, origin, birth	generation
-gnos-	know	diagnostic
-lys-	break down	analysis

Latin Root	Meaning	Sample Words
-cap-, -capt-, -cept-, -cip-	take	capitulate, captive, concept, recipient
-cede-, -ceed-, -ceas-, -cess-	happen, yield, go	precede, proceed, decease, cessation
-fac-, -fact-, -fect-, -fic-, -fy-	make	faculty, artifact, defect, beneficial, clarify
-tac-, -tag-, -tang-, -teg-	touch	contact, contagious, tangible, integral
-tain-, -ten-, -tin-	hold, keep	contain, tenure, retinue

For more prefixes, suffixes, and roots, visit **vocabularyworkshop.com**.

VOCABULARY AND READING

Word knowledge is essential to reading comprehension. Your knowledge of word meanings and ability to think carefully about what you read will help you succeed in school and on standardized tests, including the SAT, the ACT, and the PSAT.

New **Reading Passages** provide extra practice with vocabulary words. Vocabulary words are boldfaced to draw students' attention to their uses and contexts. Context clues embedded in the passages encourage students to figure out the meanings of words before they read the definitions provided on the pages directly following the passages.

Students read excerpts from classic literature in the **Vocabulary in Context** exercises. Each excerpt includes one of the Unit vocabulary words as it is used in the original work. Students can use what they learn about the word from its use in context to answer questions on the definition.

The **Vocabulary for Comprehension** exercises in each review consist of a nonfiction reading passage followed by comprehension questions. The passages and questions are similar to those that you are likely to find on standardized tests.

Kinds of Questions

Main Idea Questions generally ask what the passage as a whole is about. Often, but not always, the main idea is stated in the first paragraph of the passage. You may also be asked the main idea of a specific paragraph. Questions about the main idea may begin like this:

- The primary or main purpose of the passage is. . .
- The passage is best described as. . .
- The title that best describes the content of the passage is. . .

Detail Questions focus on important information that is explicitly stated in the passage. Often, however, the correct answer choices do not use the exact language of the passage. They are instead restatements, or paraphrases, of the text.

Vocabulary-in-Context Questions check your ability to use context to identify a word's meaning. Use line references to see how and in what context the word is used. For example:

- **Eminent** (line 8) is best defined as. . .
- The meaning of **diffuse** (line 30) is. . .

Use context to check your answer choices, particularly when the vocabulary word has more than one meaning. Among the choices may be two (or more) correct meanings of the word in question. Choose the meaning that best fits the context.

Inference Questions ask you to make inferences or draw conclusions from the passage. These questions often begin like this:

- It can be inferred from the passage that. . .
- The author implies that. . .
- Evidently the author feels that. . .

The inferences you make and the conclusions you draw must be based on the information in the passage. Your own knowledge and reasoning come into play in understanding what is implied and in reaching conclusions that are logical.

Questions About Tone show your understanding of the author's attitude toward the subject of the passage. Words that describe tone, or attitude, are "feeling" words, such as *indifferent, ambivalent, scornful, astonished, respectful*. These are typical questions:

- The author's attitude toward . . . is best described as. . .
- Which word best describes the author's tone?

To determine the tone, pay attention to the author's word choice. The author's attitude may be positive (respectful), negative (scornful), or neutral (ambivalent).

Questions About Author's Technique focus on the way a text is organized and the language the author uses. These questions ask you to think about structure and function. For example:

- The final paragraph serves to. . .
- The author cites . . . in order to . . . .

To answer the questions, you must demonstrate an understanding of the way the author presents information and develops ideas.

Strategies

Here are some general strategies to help you as you read each passage and answer the questions.

- Read the introduction first. The introduction will provide a focus for the selection.

- Be an active reader. As you read, ask yourself questions about the passage—for example: What is this paragraph about? What does the writer mean here? Why does the writer include this information?

- Refer to the passage when you answer the questions. In general, the order of the questions mirrors the organization of the passage, and many of the questions include paragraph or line references. It is often helpful to go back and reread before choosing an answer.

- Read carefully, and be sure to base your answer choices on the passage. There are answer choices that make sense but are not based on the information in the passage. These are true statements, but they are incorrect answers. The correct answers are either restatements of ideas in the text or inferences that can be drawn from the text.

- Consider each exercise a learning experience. Keep in mind that your ability to answer the questions correctly shows as much about your understanding of the questions as about your understanding of the passage.

WORKING WITH ANALOGIES

A verbal analogy expresses a relationship or comparison between sets of words. Normally, an analogy contains two pairs of words linked by a word or symbol that stands for an equal (=) sign. A complete analogy compares the two pairs of words and makes a statement about them. It asserts that the relationship between the first—or key—pair of words is the same as the relationship between the second pair.

In the **Analogies** exercises in the Final Mastery Test, you will be asked to complete analogies—that is, to choose the pair of words that best matches or parallels the relationship of the key, or given, pair of words. Here are two examples:

1. **maple** is to **tree** as
   a. acorn is to oak
   b. hen is to rooster
   c. rose is to flower
   d. shrub is to lilac

2. **joyful** is to **gloomy** as
   a. cheerful is to happy
   b. strong is to weak
   c. quick is to famous
   d. hungry is to starving

In order to find the correct answer to exercise 1, you must first determine the relationship between the two key words, **maple** and **tree**. In this case, that relationship might be expressed as "a maple is a kind (or type) of tree." The next step is to select from choices a, b, c, and d the pair of words that best reflects the same relationship. The correct answer is (c); it is the only pair whose relationship parallels the one in the key words: A rose is a kind (or type) of flower, just as a maple is a kind (or type) of tree. The other choices do not express the same relationship.

In exercise 2, the relationship between the key words can be expressed as "joyful means the opposite of gloomy." Which of the choices best represents the same relationship? The answer is (b): "strong means the opposite of weak."

Here are examples of some other common analogy relationships:

Analogy	Key Relationship
big is to **large** as **little** is to **small**	**Big** means the same thing as **large**, just as **little** means the same thing as **small**.
brave is to **favorable** as **cowardly** is to **unfavorable**	The tone of **brave** is **favorable**, just as the tone of **cowardly** is **unfavorable**.
busybody is to **nosy** as **klutz** is to **clumsy**	A **busybody** is by definition someone who is **nosy**, just as a **klutz** is by definition someone who is **clumsy**.
cowardly is to **courage** as **awkward** is to **grace**	Someone who is **cowardly** lacks **courage**, just as someone who is **awkward** lacks **grace**.
visible is to **see** as **audible** is to **hear**	If something is **visible**, you can by definition **see** it, just as if something is **audible**, you can by definition **hear** it.
liar is to **truthful** as **bigot** is to **fair-minded**	A **liar** is by definition not likely to be **truthful**, just as a **bigot** is by definition not likely to be **fair-minded**.
eyes are to **see** as **ears** are to **hear**	You use your **eyes** to **see** with, just as you use your **ears** to **hear** with.

There are many different kinds of relationships represented in the analogy questions you will find in the Final Mastery Test, but the key to solving any analogy is to find and express the relationship between the two key words.

*Read the following selection, taking note of the **boldface** words and their contexts. These words are among those you will be studying in Unit 1. As you complete the exercises in this unit, it may help to refer to the way the words are used below.*

The Globe Theatre: Then and Now

<Historical Nonfiction>

Do you laugh and **gape** at the antics of TV reality-show stars? Chances are you would have done more than that at a performance at the Globe Theatre, circa 1600. Today's dubious celebrities have nothing on the old Globe's daring actors and their raucous, rowdy audiences. In Elizabethan London, many in the ruling class viewed theatrical productions as dangerous. They thought theaters—and actors themselves—threatened the common good. That's why theaters were banished to the city's seedier neighborhoods. Built on the south banks of the River Thames in 1599, the Globe was one of the more famous theaters of its day. It was part-owned by William Shakespeare, and aristocrats and commoners alike came to see his plays. If these playgoers were lucky, they might also see Shakespeare himself.

The open-roofed Globe could hold up to 3,000 people. At the base of the apron stage (a raised platform with the audience on three sides), there was a pit where people—called "groundlings"—would stand and watch the play for a penny. Those who paid slightly more to sit in the stadium-style seats had to tread **warily**, or risk falling into the pit. The actors were almost always men, playing both male and female parts. Audience members were both **unkempt** and unruly, so actors had to endure the insults, taunts, and **gibes** of the rambunctious crowd—and often had to dodge the rotten produce hurled at them.

The Globe continued to thrive even after Shakespeare's death in 1616. It remained a lively and exciting place, but the **dour**, **stolid** Puritans in power disapproved of playacting. Their strict, joyless views on life contrasted with the Globe's **opulent**, rollicking productions, which were considered **insidious** and corrupting.

Left: William Shakespeare, 1564-1616

Background: The original Globe Theatre

So in 1642, Parliament ordered the Globe and all other London theaters closed. Constables were **deployed** to enforce the rule, actors were punished and even jailed, and anyone caught attending a play was fined. The building was dismantled, and those long-ago theater lovers were left **bereft**.

More than three centuries later, the American actor and director Sam Wanamaker went looking for the remains of this historic theater. He was appalled to find only a dirty plaque that read, "This is on or around where Shakespeare had his Globe." Wanamaker started the Shakespeare Globe Trust in 1970 to raise funds to rebuild Shakespeare's historic theater. Not everyone was convinced of his vision. Early support was **tentative**. What some called a replica of the Globe, others dismissed as a theme park that would **adulterate** Shakespeare's legacy. But Wanamaker's **fortitude** and perseverance paid off: In 1997, Shakespeare's Globe officially opened near the site of the original. The modern Globe has proven the doubters wrong—if anything, it **augments** Shakespeare's reputation as the greatest playwright of all time.

Today, the new Globe plays to packed houses. While most seasons emphasize the works of Shakespeare, often performed **verbatim**, contemporary plays are also featured. The Bard, renowned for his love of mischief, might have approved of a recent production of *Much Ado About Nothing*, one featuring an all-female cast in the **guise** of princes, lords, and soldiers. Shakespeare's Globe transports us back to the experience of theater as it was 400 years ago. Yet occasional hints of modern life, such as jets flying overhead during performances, remind us that the Globe Theatre is part of 21st century London— and not just a footnote in history books.

Inset: Eamonn Walker in *Othello*;
Background: The reconstructed Globe Theatre

iWords

Snap the code, or go to
vocabularyworkshop.com

Definitions

Note the spelling, pronunciation, part(s) of speech, and definition(s) of each of the following words. Then write the word in the blank spaces in the illustrative sentence(s) following. Finally, study the lists of synonyms and antonyms.

1. adulterate
(ə dəl′ tə rāt)

(*v.*) to corrupt, make worse by the addition of something of lesser value

Hospitals take strict precautions to assure that nothing _____ the blood supply.

SYNONYMS: contaminate, pollute, sully
ANTONYMS: purify, purge, expurgate

2. ambidextrous
(am bi dek′ strəs)

(*adj.*) able to use both hands equally well; very skillful; deceitful, hypocritical

Occasionally a teacher will come across a child who displays _____ abilities when taught to write.

SYNONYMS: versatile, flexible
ANTONYMS: clumsy, all thumbs

3. augment
(ôg ment′)

(*v.*) to make larger, increase

Many couples have to _____ their income in order to pay the mortgage on a new home.

SYNONYMS: supplement, amplify
ANTONYMS: decrease, diminish

4. bereft
(bi reft′)

(*adj., part.*) deprived of; made unhappy through a loss

Individuals who live to be very old may eventually find themselves completely _____ of friends and family.

SYNONYM: bereaved
ANTONYMS: replete, well provided

5. deploy
(di ploi′)

(*v.*) to position or arrange; to utilize; to form up

A bugle call is a signal used to _____ troops for inspection, parade, or battle.

SYNONYMS: station, organize

6. dour
(daúr)

(*adj.*) stern, unyielding, gloomy, ill-humored

Dickens's Mr. Gradgrind in the novel *Hard Times* is an example of a character with a _____ and sullen disposition.

SYNONYMS: harsh, bleak, forbidding, saturnine
ANTONYMS: cheery, inviting, genial

7. fortitude
(fôr' ti tüd)

(*n.*) courage in facing difficulties

The residents of the Mississippi delta showed remarkable

_____ during and after the flood that
destroyed their homes and businesses.

SYNONYMS: resolve, steadfastness, mettle
ANTONYMS: fearfulness, faintheartedness

8. gape
(gāp)

(*v.*) to stare with open mouth; to open the mouth wide; to
open wide

First-time visitors to Niagara Falls can be expected to

_____ at the spectacular sights nature has
provided for them.

SYNONYM: ogle

9. gibe
(jīb)

(*v.*) to utter taunting words; (*n.*) an expression of scorn

The recruits rushed into battle so that no one could

_____ at them for cowardice.

Voters may reject a candidate who resorts to personal

_____ instead of discussing the issues.

SYNONYMS: (*v.*) ridicule, mock, deride, jeer
ANTONYMS: (*n.*) compliment, praise

10. guise
(gīz)

(*n.*) an external appearance, cover, mask

The thieves gained entry to the home by presenting
themselves in the _____ of police officers.

SYNONYMS: costume, semblance, pretense

11. insidious
(in sid' ē əs)

(*adj.*) intended to deceive or entrap; sly, treacherous

The investigators uncovered an _____
scheme to rob people of their life savings.

SYNONYMS: cunning, dastardly, perfidious
ANTONYMS: frank, ingenuous, aboveboard

12. intimation
(in tə mā' shən)

(*n.*) a hint, indirect suggestion

They were too proud to give any _____ of
their financial difficulties.

SYNONYMS: clue, inkling

13. opulent
(äp' yə lənt)

(*adj.*) wealthy, luxurious; ample; grandiose

The tour guide showed us the _____ living
quarters of the royal family.

SYNONYMS: rich, plentiful, abundant
ANTONYMS: poverty-stricken, wretched, destitute

14. pliable
(plī' ə bəl)

(*adj.*) easily bent, flexible; easily influenced

Spools of _____ copper wire are standard equipment for many kinds of maintenance workers, including electricians.

SYNONYMS: adaptable, resilient
ANTONYMS: inflexible, recalcitrant

15. reiterate
(rē it' ə rāt)

(*v.*) to say again, repeat

Effective speakers often _____ an important statement for emphasis.

SYNONYMS: restate, recapitulate

16. stolid
(stäl' id)

(*adj.*) not easily moved mentally or emotionally; dull, unresponsive

_____ people can generally be expected to take most things in stride.

SYNONYMS: impassive, phlegmatic
ANTONYMS: emotional, oversensitive

17. tentative
(ten' tə tiv)

(*adj.*) experimental in nature; uncertain, hesitant

Negotiators have come up with a _____ agreement that will keep both sides at the bargaining table past the strike deadline.

SYNONYMS: provisional, inconclusive
ANTONYMS: conclusive, confirmed

18. unkempt
(ən kempt')

(*adj.*) not combed; untidy; not properly maintained; unpolished, rude

According to my parents, the latest fashions make me and my friends look _____.

SYNONYMS: sloppy, disordered, rough
ANTONYMS: well-groomed, tidy

19. verbatim
(vər bā' təm)

(*adj.*, *adv.*) word for word; exactly as written or spoken

Newspapers often publish the _____ text of an important political speech.

At the swearing-in ceremony, the Chief Justice reads each line of the Oath of Office, and the new President repeats the oath _____.

SYNONYMS: (*adj.*) exact; (*adv.*) precisely
ANTONYM: (*adj.*) paraphrased

20. warily
(wâr' ə lē)

(*adv.*) cautiously, with great care

The hikers made their way _____ up the steep and rocky trail.

SYNONYMS: prudently, gingerly
ANTONYMS: recklessly, heedlessly, incautiously

Choosing the Right Word

*Select the **boldface** word that better completes each sentence. You might refer to the essay on pages 12–13 to see how most of these words are used in context.*

1. Cassius, Brutus, and the other conspirators against Julius Caesar had developed a(n) (**opulent, insidious**) plot to assassinate the Roman dictator on the Senate floor.

2. Because the situation is changing so rapidly, any plans we make to deal with the emergency can be no more than (**verbatim, tentative**).

3. I must have been (**bereft, pliable**) of my senses when I bought that old car!

4. The speaker (**deployed, adulterated**) all the facts and figures at her command to buttress her argument.

5. I soon found out that my supposed friend had taken it upon himself to repeat (**unkempt, verbatim**) every word I said about Frieda's party.

Marble bust of Roman ruler Julius Caesar, assassinated on March 15, 44 B.C.

6. How annoying to hear the same silly advertising slogans (**gaped, reiterated**) endlessly on television!

7. By studying the reactions of simpler life forms, researchers have greatly (**adulterated, augmented**) our knowledge of human behavior.

8. Do you believe that the curriculum has been (**deployed, adulterated**) by the inclusion of courses on aspects of popular culture?

9. A sort of heaviness in the air and an eerie silence were the first real (**reiterations, intimations**) of the approaching cyclone.

10. Have you heard the joke about the (**ambidextrous, opulent**) loafer who was equally adept at not working with either hand?

11. One of the chief reasons for your dateless weekends is undoubtedly your (**opulent, unkempt**) appearance.

12. Do you expect me to listen to a lot of tired old ideas dressed up in the (**fortitude, guise**) of brilliant new insights?

13. What they call their "(**insidious, pliable**) outlook on life" seems to be simply a lack of any firm moral standards.

14. Recruits who complain of the cold should try to show a little more (**fortitude, intimation**) in facing the elements.

15. There we were at the very edge of the cliff, with our front wheels about to plunge into a(n) (**gaping, intimating**) ravine!

16. Let us not forget that the early fighters for women's rights were greeted with the (**gibes, guises**) of the unthinking mob.

17. The young prince, who much preferred blue jeans, had to dress in the (**stolid, opulent**) robes designed for the coronation.

18. Because of my inexperience, I did not recognize at first his (**insidious, ambidextrous**) attempts to undermine our employer's confidence in me.

19. The ticking grew louder as the bomb squad (**warily, pliably**) opened the package found on the grounds of the governor's residence.

20. In this scene of wild jubilation, my (**stolid, tentative**) roommate continued to eat his peanut butter sandwich as though nothing had happened.

21. The librarian hoped to (**deploy, augment**) the rare book collection by purchasing a first edition of Walt Whitman's book of poetry, *Leaves of Grass.*

22. To make beaded jewelry, it is essential that the materials you use to thread the beads, such as fine gauge wire, silk, leather, or cord, be (**pliable, ambidextrous**) and easy to work with.

23. When the famous pop star appeared at a local restaurant and began playing her guitar, it was difficult for the patrons not to (**gape, adulterate**).

24. Though all hope of victory had faded, the remaining troops continued to resist the enemy with a (**bereft, dour**) tenacity.

25. The proctor (**intimated, reiterated**) the directions for the test before we began.

 **Synonyms**

*Choose the word from this unit that is the same or most nearly the same in meaning as the **boldface** word or expression in the phrase. Write that word on the line. Use a dictionary if necessary.*

1. the **supple** limbs of a dancer _____

2. a **facile** and graceful writer _____

3. **gawk** at the huge jaws of the crocodile _____

4. gave no **indication** of being nervous _____

5. **rehash** the same old theories _____

6. **post** the remaining guards at the exits _____

7. attend a **lavish** holiday banquet _____

8. proceed **carefully** in unknown waters _____

9. need to **enlarge** the computer's memory _____

10. an **underhanded** attack on my good name _____

Antonyms

*Choose the word from this unit that is most nearly opposite in meaning to the **boldface** word or expression in the phrase. Write that word on the line. Use a dictionary if necessary.*

1. a person with a **rigid** viewpoint

2. his **direct statement** to the board of directors

3. **refused to repeat** the joke

4. surprisingly **maladroit** handling of the ball

5. a **definite** date for the party

Completing the Sentence

From the words in this unit, choose the one that best completes each of the following sentences. Write the word in the space provided.

1. How can you tell whether the chopped-meat patty you ate for lunch had been _____ with artificial coloring and other foreign substances?

2. Many ballplayers can bat from either side of the plate, but they cannot throw well with each hand unless they are _____.

3. The company commander called his troops together and asked for more volunteers to _____ the strength of the raiding party.

4. Perhaps I would be bored with the _____ lifestyle of a millionaire, but I'm willing to try it.

5. Why would someone who is usually so neat and well-dressed appear in public in such a(n) _____ state?

6. As the magician's assistant seemed to vanish into thin air, the entire audience _____ in amazement.

7. Why should I be the object of all those _____ just because I'm wearing a three-piece suit on campus?

8. In Shakespeare's famous tragedy *Othello*, Iago comes to Othello in the _____ of a friend but proves to be a deadly enemy.

9. I recorded the speaker's presentation, but now I wish I had a software program that could help me transcribe the speech _____ so that I can find appropriate quotations to use in my report.

10. America's earliest settlers faced the hardships of life on the frontier with faith and _____.

11. Having learned to respect the power in his opponent's fists, the boxer moved _____ around the center of the ring.

12. Since his acceptance of the invitation was only _____ , the host may be one man short at the dinner party.

13. Her unchanging facial features and controlled voice as she received the news gave no _____ of her true feelings.

14. What a tragedy that in the twilight of her life the unfortunate woman should be _____ of all her loved ones!

15. At the risk of being boring, let me _____ my warning against careless driving.

16. The _____ expressions on the jurors' faces as they grimly filed back into the courtroom did not bode well for the defendant.

17. We learned that beneath his _____ exterior there was a sensitive, highly subtle, and perceptive mind.

18. To this day, historians are still debating whether or not Aaron Burr was guilty of a(n) _____ plot to break up the United States.

19. The twigs that were to be woven into the basket were soaked in water to make them more _____ .

20. An experienced baseball manager _____ his outfielders according to the strengths and weaknesses of the opposing batters.

Writing: Words in Action

1. Look back at "The Globe Theatre: Then and Now" (pages 12–13). Suppose that you are Sam Wanamaker's assistant in 1970, helping him to raise funds to rebuild Shakespeare's Globe Theater. You want to persuade donors to help restore the historic theater by convincing them of three ways in which a replica of the Globe would be a cultural asset not only to London but also to the world. Write a persuasive letter, using at least two details from the passage and three unit words to make your point.

2. Think about how the experience of attending live theater is different from the experience of going to a movie theater. Write a brief essay in which you compare and contrast watching a play at a theater or playhouse to watching a film at a movie theater. Use examples from your reading (refer to pages 12–13), personal experiences, and prior knowledge to support your points of comparison. Use three or more words from this unit.

Vocabulary in Context

Literary Text

The following excerpts are from Charles Dickens's novel A Tale of Two Cities. *Some of the words you have studied in this unit appear in* **boldface** *type. Complete each statement below the excerpt by circling the letter of the correct answer.*

1. The wretched wife of the innocent man thus doomed to die, fell under the sentence, as if she had been mortally stricken. But, she uttered no sound; and so strong was the voice within her, representing that it was she of all the world who must uphold him in his misery and not **augment** it, that it quickly raised her, even from that shock.

   Someone who does NOT **augment** misery tries to

   a. reduce it   c. intensify it
   b. modify it   d. ignore it

2. Affected, and impressed with terror as they both were, by this spectacle of ruin, it was not a time to yield to such emotions. His lonely daughter, **bereft** of her final hope and reliance, appealed to them both too strongly.

   A person who is **bereft** of hope is one who has

   a. failed to act   c. moved forward
   b. tried to help   d. given up

3. Next followed the thought that much of the future peace of mind enjoyable by the dear ones, depended on his quiet **fortitude**. So, by degrees he calmed into the better state, when he could raise his thoughts much higher, and draw comfort down.

   Fortitude means

   a. intelligence   c. determination
   b. limitations   d. defenses

4. The gentleman from Tellson's had nothing left for it but to empty his glass with an air of **stolid** desperation, settle his odd little flaxen wig at the ears, and follow the waiter to Miss Manette's apartment.

   A **stolid** act is one that is

   a. brave   c. arrogant
   b. unemotional   d. exaggerated

A still from the 1935 film *A Tale of Two Cities*, with Ronald Colman as Sydney Carton

5. East, West, North, and South, through the woods, four heavy-treading, **unkempt** figures crushed the high grass and cracked the branches, striding on cautiously to come together in the courtyard.

   Someone who is **unkempt** is

   a. orderly   c. disheveled
   b. loud   d. malicious

Interactive Quiz

Snap the code, or go to **vocabularyworkshop.com**

*Read the following selection, taking note of the **boldface** words and their contexts. These words are among those you will be studying in Unit 2. As you complete the exercises in this unit, it may help to refer to the way the words are used below.*

Fashion Victims
<Informational Essay>

Some people spend a lot of time **scrutinizing** the image their clothes project. As the saying goes, "Clothes make the man." Some outfits are practical, **impervious** to rain or wind or sun or biting insects, while other outfits are chosen to express the **quintessence** of the wearer. People may not always be aware of it, but clothes offer hints about wealth, status, and even political standing. For as long as humans have worn clothes, **adroit** observers have discerned these clues.

Color

The color of clothes often tells a story. For millennia, societies around the world **extolled** the color purple. It came to represent royalty, wealth, and power because dyeing cloth purple required expensive ingredients. Ancient Greek writers were **meticulous** when describing the recipe for purple dye, a product derived from mollusks. For one gram of dye, the Greeks needed nearly 10,000 shellfish. Thus, obtaining purple clothing was not **feasible** for any but the wealthiest people. Chinese officials in the Tang Dynasty also favored purple robes, which were dyed with ingredients from a different mollusk. With the expansion of the Spanish empire in the 16th century, purple found a near rival in a deep, bright crimson, which came from a dye made of crushed cochineal insects found in Central and South America. After the British army adopted red, the soldiers sent into battle came to be known as the **belligerent** army of Redcoats.

White, in many cultures, suggests purity and spirituality. In the African countries of Nigeria and Zambia, people wear white for good luck at joyous occasions, but it is the color of bereavement in India and Asia. In Europe and the United States today, black is the color of mourning. Dyers in days gone by saturated cloth many times to ensure the darkest possible color. Because the dyeing process was labor intensive and thus expensive, only wealthy Europeans could afford black cloth.

Tyrians made purple dye from the murex shellfish.

Social and Political Status

Throughout the world, rulers historically passed laws that controlled their subjects' consumption of certain foods, building materials, and clothing. Rule breakers put their freedoms in **jeopardy**. In ancient Rome, only citizens could wear togas—and usually only in the natural off-white color of wool. Citizens running for public office could bleach their togas white, so even a **cursory** glance told the observer who was running for office. These Romans came to be known as *candidati*, or "extra white" men. In Revolutionary-era France, in the late 1700s, the *sans culottes* became a political force and participants in the country's revolution. *Sans culottes* means "without breeches." Wealthy people rode horseback and so wore breeches. The *sans culottes* were working class and wore trousers.

Eventually, laws that restricted consumption disappeared in every area but fashion, but this was not the result of the edicts of **benevolent** rulers. The **impetus** that drove such laws had been the desire to segregate people into visible, hierarchical categories. Regulations on fashions were designed to penalize **duplicity** among commoners, who might try to get ahead by dressing like aristocrats. For years, rulers believed that people who dressed as they wished would not be **amicable** subjects. Yet even as support for these laws turned **tepid** and they fell into disuse, purple remained the prerogative of the wellborn and wealthy until 1856. That's when an 18-year-old Englishman named William Perkin developed an inexpensive artificial dye of intense purple, which made the color, like fashion itself, accessible to all.

The *sans culottes* were French Revolutionaries.

iWords

Snap the code, or go to **vocabularyworkshop.com**

Different styles of Roman togas signaled a citizen's social status.

Definitions

Note the spelling, pronunciation, part(s) of speech, and definition(s) of each of the following words. Then write the word in the blank spaces in the illustrative sentence(s) following. Finally, study the lists of synonyms and antonyms.

1. adroit
(ə droit')

(*adj.*) skillful, expert in the use of the hands or mind

Many rodeo performers are _____ at twirling a rope while on horseback.

SYNONYMS: clever, deft, slick, dexterous
ANTONYMS: clumsy, inept, all thumbs

2. amicable
(am' ə kə bəl)

peaceable, friendly

(*adj.*) peaceable, friendly

Sometimes mediation by a neutral individual can lead to an _____ settlement of a dispute.

SYNONYMS: congenial, neighborly, cordial
ANTONYMS: hostile, antagonistic

3. averse
(ə vərs')

(*adj.*) having a deep-seated distaste; opposed, unwilling

You are not likely to become a marathon runner if you are _____ to strenuous exercise.

SYNONYMS: disinclined, loath
ANTONYMS: favorably disposed, eager, keen

4. belligerent
(bə lij' ə rənt)

agresive, has to do with war.

(*adj.*) given to fighting, warlike; combative, aggressive; (*n.*) one at war, one engaged in war

I did not expect such a _____ answer to my request for directions.

After each _____ signed the peace treaty, the war was declared officially over.

SYNONYMS: (*adj.*) assertive, truculent, pugnacious
ANTONYMS: (*adj.*) peaceful, conciliatory, placid

5. benevolent
(bə nev' ə lənt)

Charitable, kind

(*adj.*) kindly, charitable

The newcomers had nothing but _____ feelings toward all their neighbors.

SYNONYMS: benign, well-meaning
ANTONYMS: malicious, spiteful

6. cursory
(ker' sə rē)

hasty, not thorough quick

(*adj.*) hasty, not thorough

The mayor gave a final _____ glance at the text of her speech before mounting the podium.

SYNONYMS: quick, superficial, perfunctory
ANTONYMS: thorough, painstaking, careful

7. duplicity
(dü plis′ ə tē)

(*n.*) treachery, deceitfulness
We found it difficult to believe that our good friend could be capable of such _____.
SYNONYMS: double-dealing, chicanery

8. extol
(ek stōl′)

(*v.*) to praise extravagantly
Many inspiring stories and plays have been written that _____ the heroic deeds of Joan of Arc.
SYNONYMS: glorify, applaud, acclaim, hail
ANTONYMS: criticize, belittle, disparage

9. feasible
(fē′ zə bəl)

(*adj.*) possible, able to be done
Our city needs to develop a _____ plan of action for dealing with storms and other emergencies.
SYNONYMS: workable, viable
ANTONYMS: unworkable, impractical

possible, able to be done

10. grimace
(grim′ əs)

(*n.*) a wry face, facial distortion; (*v.*) to make a wry face
The _____ of the refugee in the photograph reveals the pain of homelessness.
Most people _____ at the mere sound of the dentist's drill.
SYNONYMS: (*n.*) pained expression, facial contortion
ANTONYMS: (*n.*) grin; (*v.*) beam

Pained expression

11. holocaust
(häl′ ə kôst)

(*n.*) a large-scale destruction, especially by fire; a vast slaughter; a burnt offering
Journalists at the time were eager to interview survivors of the Chicago _____.
SYNONYMS: conflagration, devastation, annihilation
ANTONYM: deluge

12. impervious
(im pər′ vē əs)

(*adj.*) not affected or hurt by; admitting of no passage or entrance
It is best to store flour in a container with a plastic cover that is _____ to moisture.
SYNONYMS: impenetrable, resistant, proof against
ANTONYMS: porous, permeable, vulnerable

13. impetus
(im′ pə təs)

(*n.*) a moving force, impulse, stimulus
The coming of winter gave a new _____ to the appeals for food and clothing for needy families.
SYNONYMS: impulse, spur
ANTONYMS: curb, hindrance, impediment, constraint

impulse

14. jeopardy
(jep′ ər dē)

(*n.*) danger
Experienced mountaineers know that a single mistake can put an entire expedition in serious _____.
SYNONYMS: risk, hazard, peril
ANTONYMS: safety, security

15. meticulous
(mə tik′ yə ləs)

fussy

(*adj.*) extremely careful; particular about details
If you have a full-time job outside the home, you may find it exceedingly difficult to be a _____ housekeeper.
SYNONYMS: fastidious, fussy
ANTONYMS: careless, negligent, sloppy

16. nostalgia
(nä stal′ jə)

(*n.*) a longing for something past; homesickness
Looking at old scrapbooks and reading old letters can bring on a vague sense of _____ for days gone by and friends no longer near.

17. quintessence
(kwin tes′ əns)

(*n.*) the purest essence or form of something; the most typical example
Risking one's own life to save the lives of others is considered the _____ of selfless valor.
SYNONYMS: paragon, exemplar

18. retrogress
(re trə gres′)

(*v.*) to move backward; to return to an earlier condition
In the novel, the survivors of a nuclear explosion _____ into a state of barbarism and anarchy.
SYNONYMS: revert, degenerate, decline
ANTONYMS: advance, evolve, progress

19. scrutinize
(skrüt′ ə nīz)

inspect

(*v.*) to examine closely
Lawyers are paid to _____ legal papers and explain the fine print to their clients.
SYNONYMS: inspect, pore over
ANTONYMS: scan, glance at

20. tepid
(tep′ id)

(*adj.*) lukewarm; unenthusiastic, marked by an absence of interest
A cup of _____ tea will not warm you up on a chilly morning.
SYNONYMS: insipid, halfhearted
ANTONYMS: heated, enthusiastic

Choosing the Right Word

*Select the **boldface** word that better completes each sentence. You might refer to the essay on pages 22–23 to see how most of these words are used in context.*

1. Because I was not even born when The Beatles were at the height of their popularity, their albums do not fill me with (**duplicity, nostalgia**).

The Beatles helped define the music and culture of the 1960s.

2. It was rude of you to (**retrogress, grimace**) so obviously when the speaker mispronounced words and made grammatical errors.

3. Though it may appear rather ordinary to the casual reader, Lincoln's Gettysburg Address is to me the (**impetus, quintessence**) of eloquence.

4. Some civil engineers believe that someday it may be (**feasible, averse**) to derive a large part of our energy directly from the sun.

5. Providing a powerful defense force for our nation does not mean that we are taking a (**belligerent, meticulous**) attitude toward any other nation.

6. Though the peace talks began with an exchange of lofty sentiments, they soon (**grimaced, retrogressed**) into petty squabbling and backbiting.

7. (**Extolling, Scrutinizing**) other people's achievements is fine, but it is no substitute for doing something remarkable of your own.

8. Anyone who is (**averse, cursory**) to having a girls' hockey team in our school doesn't know what's been happening in recent years with women's sports.

9. News of famine in various parts of the world has given added (**nostalgia, impetus**) to the drive to increase food production.

10. It made me very uncomfortable to see the suspicion with which the wary customs officer (**scrutinized, extolled**) my passport.

11. After shouting at each other rather angrily, the participants in the roundtable discussion calmed down and parted (**feasibly, amicably**).

12. When I saw my sister land in a tree on her first parachute jump, my interest in learning to skydive became decidedly (**tepid, adroit**).

13. The lawyer's (**adroit, belligerent**) questioning slowly but surely revealed the weaknesses in his opponent's case.

14. Carelessness in even minor details may (**extol, jeopardize**) the success of a major theatrical production.

15. Do you think you are being fair in passing judgment on my poem after such a (**cursory, benevolent**) reading?

16. His parents tried to encourage an interest in literature, music, and art, but he seemed (**amicable, impervious**) to such influences.

17. The nightmare that continues to haunt all thoughtful people is a nuclear (**jeopardy, holocaust**) in which our civilization might be destroyed.

18. In the Sherlock Holmes stories, we read of the evil Professor Moriarty, whose (**duplicity, quintessence**) was almost a match for Holmes's genius.

19. On the morning of the picnic, the sky was gray and overcast, but suddenly the sun came out and smiled on us (**benevolently, adroitly**).

20. I knew you would be (**impervious, meticulous**) in caring for my plants, but I did not expect you to water them with a medicine dropper!

21. After the dictator walked out of the peace talks, the visiting diplomat tried to carry on (**amicable, belligerent**) negotiations between the two nations.

22. Many people become (**nostalgic, meticulous**) when they watch black and white movies and old serial reruns on television.

23. How many people actually enjoy drinking (**impetus, tepid**) milk before bedtime even though it is highly recommended to ease digestion?

24. (**Impervious, Duplicitous**) to everything except a rare radioactive isotope found deep in the earth, the superhero battled the giant aliens to save the world.

25. Those who are (**adroit, averse**) to seafood may enjoy the many other menu options.

Synonyms

*Choose the word from this unit that is the same or most nearly the same in meaning as the **boldface** word or expression in the phrase. Write that word on the line. Use a dictionary if necessary.*

1. her **antipathetic** response to the homeless man _____

2. a shocking case of **fraud** _____

3. rescued dozens of people from the **blazing inferno** _____

4. the intimidating **scowl** on his face _____

5. a brief spell of **yearning** _____

6. staged a **painstaking** re-creation of a famous battle _____

7. respond with a **confrontational** voice _____

8. not **practicable** during the winter months _____

9. **relapse** to a pattern of self-destructive behavior _____

10. **imperilment** caused by risky behavior _____

Antonyms

*Choose the word from this unit that is most nearly opposite in meaning to the **boldface** word or expression in the phrase. Write that word on the line. Use a dictionary if necessary.*

1. **smiled broadly** at the sight of her grandchild _____

2. the **enthusiastic** response of the fans _____

3. an **inundation** of the valley after the storm _____

4. saw them **develop** into a successful team _____

5. a **forward-looking approach** to life _____

Completing the Sentence

From the words in this unit, choose the one that best completes each of the following sentences. Write the word in the space provided.

1. If, as you claim, you really like raw oysters, why do you make such an eloquent _____ every time you swallow one?

2. Because I was looking forward to a hot bath, I was disappointed at the feeble stream of _____ water that flowed into the tub.

3. An expert from the museum _____ the painting, looking for telltale signs that would prove it to be genuine or expose it as a forgery.

4. My teacher counseled me to keep up my studies, or my performance in class might once again _____ into mediocrity.

5. If you are _____ to hard study and intensive reading, how do you expect to get through law school?

6. Only when we learned that the embezzler had tried to cast suspicion on his innocent partner did we realize the extent of his _____.

7. Although he shows no particular talent as a worker, he is exceptionally _____ at finding excuses for not doing his job.

8. We must not forget the millions of people who were ruthlessly slaughtered by the Nazis in the _____ of World War II.

9. Our physical education instructor _____ the virtues of regular exercise.

10. What good is a plastic raincoat that is _____ to water if it also prevents any body heat from escaping?

11. When I realized how bad the brakes of the old car were, I feared that our lives were in _____.

12. Although the ranchers and miners had been feuding over water rights for years, the sheriff tried to maintain _____ relations with both parties.

13. For centuries, Switzerland has avoided becoming a(n) _____ in the conflicts that have scarred the rest of Europe.

14. When I heard you speaking French so fluently, my determination to master that language received a fresh _____.

15. As the old soldier watched the parade, he was suddenly overcome with _____ for the youthful years he spent in the army.

16. A triple reverse looks mighty impressive on the chalkboard, but I doubt that the play will prove _____ on the football field.

17. The accountant's records—neat, accurate, and complete in every respect—show that she is a most _____ worker.

18. King Arthur's Knights of the Round Table were the _____ of chivalry.

19. A(n) _____ examination of my luggage was enough to show me that someone had been tampering with it.

20. No one doubted the _____ intentions of the program for community improvement, but it was ruined by mismanagement.

Writing: Words in Action

1. Look back at "Fashion Victims" (pages 22–23). Think about how clothing styles have changed over the years and how they reflect the social values of a particular time period. Write an essay in which you analyze what current clothing styles reveal about contemporary society. Use at least two details from the passage and three unit words to support your analysis.

2. Many schools require students to wear uniforms. In a brief essay, discuss the advantages and disadvantages of school uniforms. Use specific examples from your own observations, studies, reading (refer to pages 22–23), or personal experiences. Write at least three paragraphs, and use three or more words from this unit.

Vocabulary in Context
Literary Text

The following excerpts are from The Works of Edgar Allan Poe *Volumes 1 and 2 by Edgar Allan Poe. Some of the words you have studied in this unit appear in* **boldface** *type. Complete each statement below the excerpt by circling the letter of the correct answer.*

1. ...[T]he court, guiding itself by the general principles of evidence...is **averse** from swerving at particular instances. And this steadfast adherence to principle, with rigorous disregard of the conflicting exception, is a sure mode of attaining the maximum of attainable truth.... (from "The Mystery of Marie Roget")

    When people are **averse** to something, they are typically

    a. annoyed by it　　**c.** committed to it
    b. resistant to it　　**d.** resigned to it

2. Presently I took a candle, and seating myself at the other end of the room, proceeded to **scrutinize** the parchment more closely. (from "The Gold Bug")

    To **scrutinize** a document means to

    a. translate it　　**c.** illustrate it
    b. revise it　　**d.** analyze it

3. The Parisian police, so much **extolled** for acumen, are cunning, but no more.... The results attained by them...for the most part, are brought about by simple diligence and activity. (from "The Murders in the Rue Morgue")

    People who are **extolled** for a trait are generally

    a. obeyed　　**c.** respected
    b. mocked　　**d.** ignored

Edgar Allan Poe, a master of the short story form, wrote tales of the strange and mysterious.

4. It is probable that the police...examined the back of the tenement; but, if so...they did not perceive this great breadth itself, or, at all events, failed to take it into due consideration. In fact, having once satisfied themselves that no egress could have been made in this quarter, they would naturally bestow here a very **cursory** examination. (from "The Murders in the Rue Morgue")

    A **cursory** exam is one that is definitely NOT

    a. hurried　　**c.** limited
    b. leisurely　　**d.** thorough

5. In the afternoon we all called again to see the patient. His condition remained precisely the same. We had now some discussion as to the propriety and **feasibility** of awakening him; but we had little difficulty in agreeing that no good purpose would be served by so doing. (from "The Facts in the Case of M. Valdemar")

    People discuss the **feasibility** of an action to determine whether it is

    a. achievable　　**c.** genuine
    b. complex　　**d.** productive

Interactive Quiz

Snap the code, or go to
vocabularyworkshop.com

Read the following selection, taking note of the **boldface** words and their contexts. These words are among those you will be studying in Unit 3. As you complete the exercises in this unit, it may help to refer to the way the words are used below.

Finding the Facts: Techniques of Modern Crime-Scene Investigation
<Expository Essay>

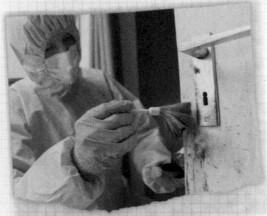

Crime-scene investigators use a special powder to "dust" for fingerprints.

Centuries ago, it was common for criminals to escape a **punitive** fate. If there were no witnesses to a crime and if the **craven** wrongdoer had run off and could not be found or could not be **coerced** into confessing, investigators had to rely on both careful reasoning and observation of the crime scene. Yet it was not enough for early investigators to examine a crime scene and then withdraw in order to **muse** on what they had seen: they needed to find actual evidence to convict the criminal. Following the **precedent** set by detectives in the past, today's crime-scene sleuths **perpetuate** law-enforcement's reliance on reasoning and observation. But they also use powerful modern techniques made possible by the progress of science.

A well-known method of modern crime-scene investigation is the use of fingerprints to identify criminals.

Fingerprints are left behind when a person's hands touch an object, but such fingerprints are usually invisible to the naked eye. To find such evidence at a crime scene, investigators rely on **artifice**: They use special powders to "dust for fingerprints" on walls, doorknobs, or other surfaces. They apply powder to the surface and brush it away. If a fingerprint is in the area, some of the powder will stick to it and reveal its unique pattern. The investigators "lift" the fingerprint with sticky tape and send the tape to a crime lab, along with other objects that may contain invisible fingerprints, such as articles of clothing, knives or other **culinary** tools, or handguns. At the lab, scientists use computers to compare the new fingerprints with others they have on file. When the scientists find a match, this evidence can help prove that a suspect was at the crime scene or that he or she handled a weapon used in the crime.

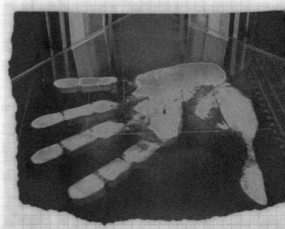

A chemical called luminol exposes blood that can't be seen after it has been washed away.

Using DNA analysis, investigators can find traces of skin or blood from a victim or criminal.

Another technique of modern crime detection is the use of chemicals like luminol to find blood at the scene. Even if a criminal has cleaned up the blood after the victim's **demise**, bloodstains are often left behind that are difficult to remove entirely. Because these bloodstains can be invisible to the naked eye, investigators use luminol to reveal their location. The investigators mix luminol powder into a liquid solution and spray it evenly onto a surface. If there are traces of blood in the sprayed area, the liquid will glow bright blue. The pattern of the bloodstain can help investigators figure out how the crime was committed, and a sample of the blood that is found is sent to the crime lab for further testing.

A more recently developed practice is the use of DNA analysis. The victim of a crime may have scratched the attacker, leaving the skin of the **adversary** under his or her fingernails. Clothing, weapons, or other objects may carry traces of blood, even if they have been cleaned or left outdoors in **inclement** weather. Even minute samples of skin, hair, or blood that once would have been considered **negligible** are now removed from the crime scene and sent to the lab to be tested for DNA. Like fingerprints, DNA testing can provide evidence connecting a suspect to the crime.

While criminals may hope to get away with their crimes, investigators continue their important work. These detectives are **exhilarated** by every scientific development that advances their ability to solve crimes. The tools of modern crime-scene investigation make it harder for criminals to avoid punishment. These tools also make it more likely that the wrongs committed by those who unfairly **harass** or harm other people will be **redressed** in a court of law. Then it is up to the judge and jury to ensure the punishment fits the crime.

Snap the code, or go to vocabularyworkshop.com

Definitions

Note the spelling, pronunciation, part(s) of speech, and definition(s) of each of the following words. Then write the word in the blank spaces in the illustrative sentence(s) following. Finally, study the lists of synonyms and antonyms.

1. adversary
(ad' vər ser ē)

(*n.*) an enemy, opponent

A best friend off the tennis court can also be a fierce _____ on it.

SYNONYMS: antagonist, foe
ANTONYMS: friend, ally, supporter, confederate

2. alienate
(ā' lē ə nāt)

(*v.*) to turn away; to make indifferent or hostile; to transfer, convey

Gossiping and backbiting are bad habits that are bound to _____ friends.

SYNONYMS: separate, drive apart, estrange
ANTONYMS: befriend, attract, captivate

3. artifice
(är' tə fis)

(*n.*) a skillful or ingenious device; a clever trick; a clever skill; trickery

Even the most renowned art experts were completely taken in by the forger's _____.

SYNONYMS: ruse, stratagem, contrivance

4. coerce
(kō ərs')

(*v.*) to compel, force

Dictators try to _____ their subjects into obedience by threatening them or their families with punishment.

SYNONYMS: pressure, bully, constrain
ANTONYMS: persuade, cajole

5. craven
(krā' vən)

(*adj.*) cowardly; (*n.*) a coward

Those who urged Great Britain to make peace with Hitler were criticized for their _____ attitude.

It is a mistake to assume that everyone who refuses to go to war is a _____ who lacks patriotism.

SYNONYMS: (*adj.*) fearful, fainthearted, pusillanimous
ANTONYMS: (*adj.*) brave, courageous, valiant

6. culinary
(kyü' lə ner ē)

(*adj.*) of or related to cooking or the kitchen

Cooking shows on television have helped many people to master the secrets of the _____ arts.

7. demise
(di mīz')

(*n.*) a death, especially of a person in a lofty position
Traditionally, the tolling of church bells has announced the
_____ of a monarch.

SYNONYMS: decease, passing away
ANTONYMS: birth, commencement

8. exhilarate
(eg zil' ə rāt)

(*v.*) to enliven, cheer, give spirit or liveliness to
The first landing on the moon, in the summer of 1969,
_____ the nation.

SYNONYMS: stimulate, excite, gladden
ANTONYMS: discourage, dispirit, dishearten, inhibit

9. fallow
(fal' ō)

(*adj.*) plowed but not seeded; inactive; reddish-yellow; (*n.*) land
left unseeded; (*v.*) to plow but not seed
After a month without a date, I decided that my social life
was definitely in a _____ period.
In the drought-stricken region, there were millions of acres
of _____.
Farmers often _____ a third of their fields
each year to restore the chemical balance of the soil.

SYNONYMS: (*adj.*) unproductive, dormant
ANTONYMS: (*adj.*) productive, fertile, prolific

10. harass
(hə ras')

(*v.*) to disturb, worry; to trouble by repeated attacks
The judge repeatedly cautioned the prosecuting attorney
not to _____ the witness.

SYNONYMS: annoy, bedevil, beleaguer

11. inclement
(in klem' ənt)

(*adj.*) stormy, harsh; severe in attitude or action
During an _____ New England winter,
heavy snowfalls may bring highway traffic to a standstill.

SYNONYMS: blustery, tempestuous, implacable
ANTONYMS: mild, gentle, balmy

12. liquidate
(lik' wi dāt')

(*v.*) to pay a debt, settle an account; to eliminate
After a profitable year, the business was able to
_____ its loan.

SYNONYMS: reconcile, pay, cancel, exterminate
ANTONYMS: invest, collect

13. muse
(myüz)

(*v.*) to think about in a dreamy way, ponder
Philosophers have always _____ on the
meaning of life.

SYNONYMS: contemplate, daydream

14. negligible
(neg′ lə jə bəl)

(*adj.*) so unimportant that it can be disregarded

After taxes are deducted, a small raise in salary may result in a _____ increase in take-home pay.

SYNONYMS: trivial, inconsequential, insignificant
ANTONYMS: significant, crucial, momentous

15. perpetuate
(pər pech′ ü āt)

(*v.*) to make permanent or long lasting

In most cultures, people try to _____ the customs of their ancestors.

SYNONYMS: continue, preserve, prolong indefinitely
ANTONYMS: discontinue, abolish, abandon

16. precedent
(pres′ ə dənt)

(*n.*) an example that may serve as a basis for imitation or later action

We hope that students at other schools in our city will follow our _____ in volunteer work and charitable contributions.

SYNONYMS: guide, tradition, model

17. punitive
(pyü′ nə tiv)

(*adj.*) inflicting or aiming at punishment

The general led a _____ expedition against the rebel forces.

SYNONYMS: penalizing, retaliatory

18. redress
(rē dres′)

(*v.*) to set right, remedy; (*n.*) relief from wrong or injury

An apology can go a long way to _____ the hurt feelings caused by an insensitive comment or a thoughtless act.

The accident victims will seek _____ for the injuries they suffered in the train crash.

SYNONYMS: (*v.*) correct, mitigate

19. sojourn
(sō′ jərn)

(*n.*) a temporary stay; (*v.*) to stay for a time

No matter how short your _____ in Paris, you must take time to go to the Louvre.

Many American graduates _____ abroad before they begin working full-time at home.

SYNONYMS: (*n.*) visit, brief stay

20. urbane
(ər bān′)

(*adj.*) refined in manner or style, suave

An _____ host puts guests at ease by appearing totally confident and unruffled no matter what happens.

SYNONYM: elegant
ANTONYMS: crude, uncouth

Choosing the Right Word

*Select the **boldface** word that better completes each sentence. You might refer to the essay on pages 32–33 to see how most of these words are used in context.*

1. When Washington refused to serve a third term as President, he set a(n) (**artifice, precedent**) that was to last for 150 years.

2. Our history shows how the (**demise, adversary**) of one political party provides an opportunity for the formation of a new one.

3. We must reject the (**craven, fallow**) advice of those who feel we can solve social problems by abandoning our democratic freedoms.

4. The critics unanimously praised the actor for the (**urbane, punitive**) charm with which he played the well-bred English gentleman.

Before he became the first president, George Washington led troops in the Revolutionary War.

5. May I remind you that the (**urbane, punitive**) action we are authorized to take does not include physical force of any kind.

6. Our city government needs basic reforms; clever little (**sojourns, artifices**) will not solve our problems.

7. Do you really expect me to believe that your friends (**coerced, alienated**) you into cutting class to go to the movies?

8. We need a supervisor who can maintain good discipline in the shop without (**harassing, exhilarating**) the workers.

9. The story takes place in a foreign country where a rogue government agent accepts a mission to (**liquidate, coerce**) an evil dictator.

10. Because of the severe sentences she often handed down, she gained the reputation of being an extremely (**negligible, inclement**) judge.

11. Only when the attempt to get the British government to (**redress, harass**) injustices proved unsuccessful did the American colonists resort to arms.

12. It is all very well to (**muse, perpetuate**) on what might have been, but it is far better to take action to make good things happen.

13. I admit that we did some foolish things after the game, but you must remember how (**mused, exhilarated**) we were by the victory.

14. Since we are making (**craven, negligible**) progress in our fight against pollution, the time has come for us to adopt completely new methods.

15. After a long (**urbane, fallow**) period during which she scarcely touched her brushes, the painter suddenly produced a series of major canvases.

16. The highlight of my trip to Europe came when I (**sojourned, redressed**) in the birthplace of my ancestors.

17. When he blocked my jump shot, took the rebound, drove down the court, and scored, I realized that I was facing a worthy (**artifice, adversary**).

18. And now I want you all to try my (**inclement, culinary**) masterpiece—a salami soufflé, garnished with sour cream.

19. The coach ran the risk of (**exhilarating, alienating**) influential graduates of the school when she suspended a star player who had broken training.

20. If we do not take steps now to clear their names, we will be (**perpetuating, liquidating**) an injustice that has already lasted far too long.

21. Did the other journalists (**alienate, perpetuate**) the young writer after she expressed some political views with which they disagreed?

22. After several months of losing money, the furniture store held a huge sale, hoping to (**liquidate, redress**) its entire inventory.

23. To rid your aquarium of parasites, allow the tank to remain (**negligible, fallow**) for several weeks, and keep your fish in a separate tank.

24. The artist took a(n) (**adversary, sojourn**) to the mountains, hoping to relieve his stress and renew his creativity.

25. (**Urbane, Craven**) and sophisticated, the young princess charmed the diplomat.

Synonyms

*Choose the word from this unit that is the same or most nearly the same in meaning as the **boldface** word or expression in the phrase. Write that word on the line. Use a dictionary if necessary.*

1. **pestered** by flies and mosquitoes _____

2. a **castigatory** campaign against a political rival _____

3. a relaxing **stopover** on a tropical island _____

4. a **polished** manner that puts people at ease _____

5. an attempt to **rectify** past mistakes _____

6. an **inert** phase in the artist's long career _____

7. to **sell off** poor stock investments _____

8. a **pretense** used to fool unwary customers _____

9. a dangerous **rival** who will stop at nothing _____

10. **isolated** from society _____

Antonyms

*Choose the word from this unit that is most nearly opposite in meaning to the **boldface** word or expression in the phrase. Write that word on the line. Use a dictionary if necessary.*

1. planned on a **permanent stay**   _____

2. unexpectedly **boorish** behavior toward others   _____

3. **reconcile with** an estranged friend   _____

4. a dialogue that is **fruitful**   _____

5. **accumulate** possessions after a shopping spree _____

Completing the Sentence

From the words in this unit, choose the one that best completes each of the following sentences. Write the word in the space provided.

1. Their _____ behavior at the first sign of danger was a disgrace to the uniform they wore.

2. There are far more subtle ways of _____ a person into doing what you want than twisting his or her arm.

3. In 1858, Abraham Lincoln held a series of debates with Stephen Douglas, his _____ in the contest for U.S. Senator from Illinois.

4. The coach took me off the starting team as a(n) _____ measure for missing two days of practice.

5. At first we watched the game with relatively little emotion, but we became so _____ by our team's strong comeback that we began to cheer loudly.

6. As I lay under the old apple tree, I began to _____ on the strange twists of fate that had led to the present situation.

7. When the snowstorm lasted into a second day, we listened attentively to the radio to find out if our school was among those closed because of the _____ weather.

8. When planning our trip to the Southwest, we made sure to set aside two days for a(n) _____ at the Grand Canyon.

9. When Grandfather stubbornly refused to eat his vegetables, he set a(n) _____ that was immediately followed by the children.

10. The _____ of an administration in the United States is never a crisis because a newly elected administration is waiting to take over.

11. If we continue to elect unworthy people to public office, we will simply _____ the evils that we have tried so hard to correct.

12. When citizens feel that something is wrong, they have a right under the First Amendment to ask their government for a(n) _____ of grievances.

13. The coach emphasized that the way to stop our opponents' passing game was to _____ their receivers and blitz their quarterback.

14. The deserted buildings and the land lying _____ hinted at the troubles the farmers in the area were experiencing.

15. Since both cars had virtually come to a halt by the time their bumpers met, the damage was _____.

16. Magicians rely on sleight of hand and other forms of _____ to deceive their unsuspecting audiences.

17. I advise you to _____ all of your assets and negotiate with creditors before declaring bankruptcy.

18. Their bad manners and insufferable conceit _____ even those who were most inclined to judge them favorably.

19. The full extent of my _____ skill is preparing scrambled eggs on toast.

20. His charmingly _____ manner and keen wit made him a much sought-after guest at social gatherings.

Writing: Words in Action

1. Look back at "Finding the Facts: Techniques of Modern Crime-Scene Investigation" (pages 32–33). Write an essay in which you compare and contrast the modern techniques of crime-scene investigation and explain which one you believe provides the most effective evidence for identifying and ultimately prosecuting criminals. Use at least two details from the passage and three unit words to support your view.

2. Forensic scientists, detectives, crime-scene investigators, and others all work in the field of criminal justice and corrections, part of the law and public safety career cluster. Numerous jobs and career paths exist in such broad fields as government, finance, health, business, transportation, information technology, agriculture, and communications, among many other areas. In a brief essay, explain what kind of career most appeals to you and how you could use your interests and skills to become successful in that career. Support your ideas with specific examples from your reading (refer to pages 32–33), your own observations, and your personal experiences. Write at least three paragraphs, and use three or more words from this unit.

Vocabulary in Context

Literary Text

The following excerpts are from **The Tenant of Wildfell Hall** *by Anne Brontë. Some of the words you have studied in this unit appear in* **boldface** *type. Complete each statement below the excerpt by circling the letter of the correct answer.*

1. "He cannot linger long. He suffers dreadfully, and so do those that wait upon him. But I will not **harass** you with further details: I have said enough, I think, to convince you that I did well to go to him."

   If you **harass** someone about an illness, you

   a. trouble her
   b. bore her
   c. comfort her
   d. cure her

2. She could not now absent herself under the plea of dark evenings or **inclement** weather, and, greatly to my relief, she came.

   Inclement weather is NOT

   a. turbulent
   b. ominous
   c. temperate
   d. unpredictable

3. ... but the moment I was out of sight of my fair tormentor cutting away across the country, just as a bird might fly, over pasture-land, and **fallow**, and stubble, and lane, clearing hedges and ditches and hurdles, till I came to the young squire's gates.

   Fallow is

   a. uncultivated land
   b. a wooded area
   c. a lush field
   d. a fast-moving stream

   Anne Brontë, the sister of Emily and Charlotte, wrote two novels before her death at age 29.

4. He has been in person to Staningley, seeking **redress** for his grievances—expecting to hear of his victims, if not to find them there—and has told so many lies, and with such unblushing coolness, that my uncle more than half believes him, and strongly advocates my going back to him and being friends again.

   A person seeking **redress** expects a

   a. greeting
   b. resolution
   c. punishment
   d. repetition

5. I did not mention my suspicions to Rachel; but she, having **sojourned** for half a century in this land of sin and sorrow, has learned to be suspicious herself.

   Someone who has **sojourned** for many years has

   a. changed drastically
   b. learned considerably
   c. traveled frequently
   d. suffered greatly

Interactive Quiz

Snap the code, or go to **vocabularyworkshop.com**

Vocabulary for Comprehension

*Read the following selection in which some of the words you have studied in Units 1–3 appear in **boldface** type. Then answer the questions on page 43.*

Celebrity chef Julia Child, the subject of the following passage, is credited with bringing French cuisine to American home cooks. She died in August 2004 at the age of 91.

(Line)

In the world of the **culinary** arts, probably no one has had a greater influence on Americans than Julia Child. She was born Julia

(5) McWilliams in Pasadena, California, in 1912. Her interest in cooking was **negligible** until she met Paul Cushing Child, an artist, diplomat, and gourmet, in China in the early

(10) 1940s. The couple married in 1946 and moved to Paris in 1948. There, Julia studied French and enrolled at the Cordon Bleu, a famous French cooking school. Soon she was an

(15) **adroit** cook and an enthusiast of classical French cuisine. Eager to share her knowledge, Julia opened a cooking school in Paris with two friends. With one of these friends,

(20) Simone Beck, she began writing a cookbook based on their experiences at the school. They continued to work on the book as Julia moved around Europe with her

(25) husband.

When Paul retired in 1961, the Childs returned to the United States and settled in Cambridge, Massachusetts. That year, Julia's first

(30) cookbook, *Mastering the Art of French Cooking*, was published in the United States. It was an immense popular and critical success. Julia Child was immediately **extolled** as

(35) an expert on French cuisine and cooking instruction. Her book was praised for its **meticulous** attention to detail, clear and complete explanations, and straightforward,

(40) unpretentious tone.

In 1963, Julia's half-hour cooking program, *The French Chef*, debuted on Boston's public television station. This award-winning show attracted

(45) an enthusiastic and ever-growing audience. Even noncooks enjoyed Julia Child's evident love of fine food, down-to-earth good humor, and easygoing manner. She had the

(50) uncommon ability to convince her viewers that it was **feasible** for them to succeed in the kitchen. She made people realize that cooking is fun.

In new cookbooks and television

(55) programs that appeared in the ensuing decades, Julia Child adapted her recipes to accommodate the contemporary desire for low-fat meals that could be

(60) prepared quickly. Yet she remained true to what she considered the essentials of fine French cuisine.

1. The primary purpose of the passage is to
   a. publicize the success of *The French Chef*
   b. pay tribute to Julia Child
   c. describe Julia Child's culinary background
   d. demystify French cuisine
   e. popularize American cuisine

2. In line 1, **culinary** most nearly means
   a. literary
   b. martial
   c. performing
   d. cooking
   e. fine

3. **Negligible** (line 7) most nearly means
   a. nonexistent
   b. sincere
   c. limited
   d. immense
   e. insignificant

4. **Adroit** (line 15) is best defined as
   a. legal
   b. amateur
   c. skillful
   d. inept
   e. sloppy

5. Evidently Julia Child's interest in cooking can be attributed, in part, to
   a. the influence of her husband
   b. her education at the Cordon Bleu
   c. her friendship with Simone Beck
   d. her early childhood
   e. a love of travel

6. In line 34, the meaning of **extolled** is
   a. identified
   b. dismissed
   c. consulted
   d. trained
   e. acclaimed

7. **Meticulous** (line 37) most nearly means
   a. honest
   b. occasional
   c. painstaking
   d. unnecessary
   e. welcome

8. **Feasible** (line 51) is best defined as
   a. possible
   b. challenging
   c. joyful
   d. unlikely
   e. important

9. One of Julia Child's notable achievements was convincing the American public that
   a. cooking is serious business
   b. anyone can cook French cuisine
   c. low-fat meals can be prepared quickly
   d. French cuisine is superior to American cuisine
   e. the Cordon Bleu is the best place to study classical French cooking

10. In the final paragraph (lines 54–62), the author presents evidence of Julia Child's
    a. inflexibility
    b. unpredictability
    c. generosity
    d. adaptability
    e. curiosity

11. Much of Julia Child's appeal lay in her
    a. unpretentious style and humor
    b. meticulous attention to nutrition
    c. extensive knowledge of American cuisine
    d. unwillingness to compromise
    e. uncommon love of all things French

12. The author's attitude toward Julia Child is best described as one of
    a. antipathy
    b. amusement
    c. admiration
    d. acceptance
    e. apathy

Two-Word Completions

Select the pair of words that best complete the meaning of each of the following passages.

1. Tony's general attitude toward people is so _____ that he has _____ absolutely everybody who knows him. If he didn't walk around with such a huge chip on his shoulder, he would have a few friends.
   a. benevolent . . . deployed
   b. impervious . . . exhilarated
   c. belligerent . . . alienated
   d. amicable . . . redressed

2. "I haven't yet had time to give your latest sales report more than a _____ glance," my boss told me. "However, I plan to _____ it carefully before we sit down to discuss it in detail."
   a. verbatim . . . reiterate
   b. cursory . . . scrutinize
   c. meticulous . . . augment
   d. tentative . . . redress

3. My first _____ of Nelson's double-dealing came when I discovered him whispering with my opponent. Prior to that, I had no inkling of my so-called friend's _____.
   a. intimation . . . duplicity
   b. scrutiny . . . fortitude
   c. precedent . . . artifice
   d. redress . . . coercion

4. Because the course of the disease was so _____, we didn't notice at first that the patient's condition was no longer improving but in fact had begun to _____.
   a. tentative . . . adulterate
   b. adroit . . . redress
   c. averse . . . perpetuate
   d. insidious . . . retrogress

5. Some people always stick up their noses at food they're not accustomed to, but I'm not at all _____ to trying something new. Still, experience has taught me to be _____ of such dubious delicacies as chocolate-covered ants, and I usually look before I leap, so to speak.
   a. amicable . . . bereft
   b. tepid . . . negligible
   c. averse . . . wary
   d. impervious . . . craven

6. I have _____ chosen an excerpt from the president's inaugural address that I'd like to use in my report. Unfortunately, the passage is far too long to reproduce _____.
   a. tentatively . . . verbatim
   b. stolidly . . . coerce
   c. meticulously . . . reiterate
   d. feasibly . . . liquidate

7. Although I now have a very _____ relationship with my older sister, she recalls that we used to fight over everything, viewing each other as _____.
   a. insidious . . . bereft
   b. cursory . . . negligible
   c. amicable . . . adversaries
   d. adulterated . . . dour

Adages

In the essay about how fashions, clothing colors, and styles have changed over the years (see pages 22–23), the author uses the old saying, "Clothes make the man."

"Clothes make the man" is an example of an adage. An **adage** is a saying passed down through the years that makes a memorable and often witty or humorous observation about some familiar aspect of life. The adage "Clothes make the man" suggests that the clothes we wear reflect how we want to be perceived by others. It also suggests that people will make judgments about a person based on how he or she dresses.

Choosing the Right Adage

Read each sentence. Use context clues to figure out the meaning of each adage in **boldface** *print. Then write the letter of the definition for the adage in the sentence.*

1. When Amy's entire family tried advising her on her science project, she politely told them that **too many cooks spoil the broth**. _____

2. Christopher resented missing outings because of his cello practice, so his father often had to remind him that **April showers bring May flowers**. _____

3. **Beggars can't be choosers**, so don't complain about the food your friends shared with you when you forgot your lunch. _____

4. **"Better safe than sorry,"** my mother said as she waited for me to fasten my seatbelt. _____

5. Because we believe **the more the merrier**, we often invite a group of friends over for movie night. _____

6. Since **misery loves company**, Chris and Ty, who had both failed to make the track team, sat together at lunch. _____

7. **Cold hands, warm heart** describes my aunt. She can be brusque and no-nonsense, but is always the first to send a thoughtful card or gift in times of trouble. _____

8. Greg had failed to sell his writing for years, but **every dog has its day**, and he finally sold his first novel. _____

9. **You can't have your cake and eat it, too**, so don't expect Kim, whom you insulted last week, to invite you to her party. _____

10. When you start a new job, **a new broom sweeps clean**, but soon the work will probably start to feel routine. _____

a. You shouldn't be picky when accepting generosity.

b. Unhappy people band together for comfort and commiseration.

c. Activities are more fun with a large group.

d. A person who does not show feelings easily can still be very kind.

e. Something new seems exciting at first.

f. You cannot have things both ways.

g. Good results often come from unpleasant things.

h. Having too many helpers on a project can ruin the result.

i. Eventually, everyone has a chance for success or luck.

j. Practicing caution can prevent suffering later.

Writing with Adages

Find the meaning of each adage. (Use an online or print dictionary if necessary.)
Then write a sentence for each adage.

1. Time is money.

_____

2. business before pleasure

_____

3. Stop and smell the roses.

_____

4. easy come, easy go

_____

5. The best things in life are free.

_____

_____

6. Open mouth, insert foot.

_____

_____

7. once bitten, twice shy

_____

_____

8. The grass is always greener on the other side.

_____

9. It takes two to tango.

_____

10. The walls have ears.

_____

11. Still waters run deep.

_____

12. A penny saved is a penny earned.

_____

Denotation and Connotation

The dictionary definition or literal meaning of a word is its **denotation**. A word's denotation conveys a *neutral* tone, neither positive nor negative.

Many words have an underlying meaning, or connotation. The **connotation** of a word is an association people make with the word, usually a particular meaning or emotion that the word evokes. Connotations may be *positive* or *negative*.

Consider these synonyms for the neutral word *skillful*:

> *deft*   *adroit*   *masterful*   *slick*

Deft, *adroit*, and *masterful* have positive connotations, suggesting a high level of skill. *Slick*, on the other hand, can have a negative connotation. If a person is called *slick*, it might suggest that there is something misleading or false in his or her performance.

> **Think:** A professional magician performing card tricks may be considered deft, adroit, or masterful, but a gambler playing poker may be considered slick.

Look at these examples of words that are similar in denotation but have different connotations.

NEUTRAL	POSITIVE	NEGATIVE
affect	influence	coerce
rich	opulent	excessive
praise	extol	flatter

Words that have particularly strong connotations—emotionally "charged" positive or negative associations—are often called **loaded words**. Loaded words are common tools of persuasive writers and speakers, who understand the power of implied meanings to influence an audience's perceptions.

Shades of Meaning

Write a plus sign (+) in the box if the word has a positive connotation. Write a minus sign (−) if the word has a negative connotation. Put a zero (0) if the word is neutral.

1. insidious ☐   **2.** fortitude ☐   **3.** unkempt ☐   **4.** deploy ☐

5. culinary ☐   **6.** adulterate ☐   **7.** extol ☐   **8.** artifice ☐

9. alienate ☐   **10.** precedent ☐   **11.** grimace ☐   **12.** harass ☐

13. verbatim ☐   **14.** urbane ☐   **15.** bereft ☐   **16.** exhilarating ☐

Expressing the Connotation

Read each sentence. Select the word in parentheses that expresses the connotation (positive, negative, or neutral) given at the beginning of the sentence.

neutral
1. The speaker (**proclaimed, extolled**) the man as a true hero who went beyond the call of duty.

positive
2. Although the way you have dealt with her betrayal shows (**strength, fortitude**), I still think you must confront her.

negative
3. When the armed robber fled with the money, the sheriff did not pursue him, proving his (**craven, weak**) nature.

negative
4. The actress arrived at the charitable event wearing a(n) (**gaudy, opulent**) diamond necklace.

neutral
5. I was very pleased by how (**urbane, polite**) everyone at school was toward our visiting guest.

neutral
6. The detective approached the building (**warily, sneakily**), hoping to get close enough to take a photo without being noticed.

positive
7. The (**exhilarating, pleasing**) news about the high annual bonus motivated the employees even more.

negative
8. The flight attendant called security when the passenger became (**belligerent, difficult**).

Challenge: Using Connotation

Choose vocabulary words from Units 1–3 to replace the highlighted words in the sentences below. Then explain how the connotation of the replacement word changes the tone of the sentence.

harass	retrogress	benevolent
dour	adversary	gibe

1. The general marched toward the river, nervous about meeting his **opponent**

_____.

_____

_____

2. The student's **gloomy** _____ attitude toward his education made his parents concerned about his future.

_____

_____

3. My sister gets very annoyed when I **tease** _____ her about her boyfriend.

_____

_____

Classical Roots

mis, miss, mit—to send

The root *mis* appears in **demise** (page 35). The literal meaning is "a sending down," but the word now suggests a death, especially of a person in an elevated position. Some other words based on the same root are listed below.

commissary	emit	missile	premise
emissary	manumit	permit	remission

From the list of words above, choose the one that corresponds to each of the brief definitions below. Write the word in the blank space in the illustrative sentence below the definition. Use an online or print dictionary if necessary.

1. to free from slavery or bondage

In some ancient societies, it was the custom to _____ all children born into slavery.

2. a statement or idea upon which a conclusion is based (*"that which is sent before"*)

Some members of Congress argued that the budget proposal was based on false _____.

3. a letup, abatement; a relief from suffering

Immediately after undergoing major surgery, a patient may need some medication for the _____ of pain.

4. to consent to formally; to authorize; to allow

The law _____ a person convicted of a crime to file an appeal.

5. to release or send forth (*"send out"*)

Crickets _____ a shrill chirp by rubbing their wings together.

6. an object to be thrown or shot

The new fighter plane can fire a(n) _____ with deadly accuracy.

7. a place where supplies are distributed; a lunchroom

Campers and counselors eat their meals at the _____.

8. a messenger, agent (*"one sent out"*)

The president sent a special _____ to discuss the drafting of a peace agreement.

*Read the following selection, taking note of the **boldface** words and their contexts. These words are among those you will be studying in Unit 4. As you complete the exercises in this unit, it may help to refer to the way the words are used below.*

Patronage of the Arts: Help or Hindrance?

<Narrative Nonfiction>

"Is not a patron, my lord, one who looks with unconcern on a man struggling for life in the water, and when he has reached ground, encumbers him with help?" So wrote the British author Samuel Johnson to Lord Chesterfield in 1755. In his letter, Johnson bitterly protested the **supercilious** tone of Chesterfield's belated offer of patronage. Having lived in near-poverty while creating the first dictionary of the English language, Johnson got the last laugh: In his book, he defined *patron* as "a wretch who supports with insolence and is paid in flattery."

A **cogent** and convincing account of patronage of the arts would have to acknowledge its long, productive history. Beginning with the European Renaissance, the period from the 14th to 17th centuries, art patronage—financial support of an artist by wealthy noblemen, members of the aristocracy, and the papacy—flourished. While this system kept artists employed, the artists had to make whatever their patron wanted, whether a flattering portrait of the patron's wife or a statue of the patron in the role of a biblical figure. Artists composed poems, plays, operas, and symphonies—and hoped their patron liked the results.

The patronage system **bequeathed** countless masterpieces to future generations. Scholars have **ascertained**

numerous instances in which the needs of patron and artist **converged**: in a quest for glory, on the one hand, and for funds on the other. Two such cases are shown in the careers of Jean Racine, a French playwright, and George Frideric Handel, a music composer in England.

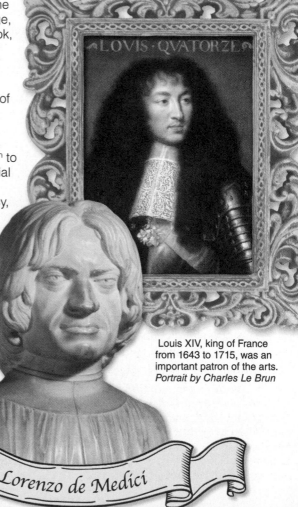

Louis XIV, king of France from 1643 to 1715, was an important patron of the arts. *Portrait by Charles Le Brun*

Lorenzo de Medici

Young Mozart at the court of Empress Maria Theresa

Jean Racine (1639–1699) was born into a middle-class family and orphaned before the age of four. By an **uncanny** stroke of good fortune, he was privileged to attend the school of Port-Royal near Paris. There, he acquired such a mastery of classical literature as to make him seem virtually **omniscient** on the subject. By the age of twenty, Racine's literary **attainments** had won the young writer considerable **esteem**. Later, Racine produced a play on the life of Alexander the Great, conveying a **scrupulous** parallel to the reign of Louis XIV, well known as a patron of the arts. Racine's goal was transparent: He wished to be **affiliated** with the royal court. Royal patronage, however, did not free even a talent like Racine from criticism. Many contemporaries regarded him as France's greatest tragic playwright, but **malevolent** rivals attacked him and called his work historically inaccurate and without drama.

In Germany, the young George Frideric Handel (1685–1759) was growing up in the town of Halle. Like Racine, Handel, a music composer, showed phenomenal talent at an early age. After three years of travel in Italy, he made his first visit to England in 1710. Within three years, he had won royal patronage at the court of

Queen Anne. He spent most his long life in England, achieving success writing many musical forms: opera, oratorio, orchestral overtures, choral anthems, and chamber music. Much of his work might not have been produced without the financial support of patronage.

Artists have always had to walk a straight line to keep their patronage. Even minor, **venial** offenses might disenchant a patron. Yet it is hard to imagine how artists such as Mozart or Michelangelo might have fared without patronage. Would their works ever have been created and widely **dispersed**? In the end, while art patronage influenced the works of some of history's greatest creators, it has also produced an infinitely rich heritage that has proved **invulnerable** to the passage of time.

iWords

Snap the code, or go to
vocabularyworkshop.com

Definitions

Note the spelling, pronunciation, part(s) of speech, and definition(s) of each of the following words. Then write the word in the blank spaces in the illustrative sentence(s) following. Finally, study the lists of synonyms and antonyms.

1. affiliated
(ə fil′ ē āt əd)

(*adj., part.*) associated, connected

Being _____ with a well-known law firm is often an important first step on the way to a successful political career.

SYNONYMS: attached, related, joined
ANTONYMS: dissociated, unconnected

2. ascertain
(as ər tān′)

(*v.*) to find out

We need to _____ what it will cost to remodel our kitchen.

SYNONYMS: discover, establish

3. attainment
(ə tān′ mənt)

(*n.*) an accomplishment, the act of achieving

In addition to his abilities as a leader, Abraham Lincoln was a man of high literary _____.

SYNONYMS: achievement, fulfillment
ANTONYMS: failure, defeat, frustration

4. bequeath
(bi kwēth′)

(*v.*) to give or pass on as an inheritance

Few people will make enough money in their lifetimes to be in a position to _____ a fortune to their heirs.

SYNONYMS: transmit, bestow

5. cogent
(kō′ jint)

(*adj.*) forceful, convincing; relevant, to the point

A group of legal scholars held a press conference to present a _____ plea for reform of the state's prison system.

SYNONYMS: persuasive, compelling
ANTONYMS: weak, unconvincing, ineffective, irrelevant

6. converge
(kən verj′)

(*v.*) to move toward one point, approach nearer together

The television coverage resumed as soon as the delegates _____ on the hall to hear the keynote speaker's address.

SYNONYMS: meet, unite, intersect, merge
ANTONYMS: diverge, separate

7. disperse
(di spərs')

(*v.*) to scatter, spread far and wide

When a scuffle broke out, the commissioner ordered the police to _____ the crowd.

SYNONYMS: break up, dispel
ANTONYMS: collect, congregate, assemble, muster

8. esteem
(es tēm')

(*v.*) to regard highly; (*n.*) a highly favorable opinion or judgment

In many of the world's cultures, young people are taught to _____ their ancestors.

The Chief Justice of the Supreme Court should be someone whom all parties hold in high _____.

SYNONYMS: (*v.*) respect, honor, revere
ANTONYMS: (*v.*) disdain, scorn; (*n.*) contempt

9. expunge
(ik spənj')

(*v.*) to erase, obliterate, destroy

The judge ordered the remarks _____ from the court record.

SYNONYMS: efface, annihilate
ANTONYMS: insert, mark, imprint, impress

10. finite
(fi' nīt)

(*adj.*) having limits; lasting for a limited time

There are only a _____ number of possible answers to a multiple-choice question.

SYNONYMS: bounded, measurable
ANTONYMS: unlimited, immeasurable, everlasting, eternal

11. invulnerable
(in vəl' nər ə bəl)

(*adj.*) not able to be wounded or hurt; shielded against attack

Medieval lords did everything possible to make their castles _____ fortresses.

SYNONYMS: impregnable, impervious, immune
ANTONYMS: exposed, unprotected, defenseless

12. malevolent
(mə lev' ə lənt)

(*adj.*) spiteful, showing ill will

While pretending to be a loyal friend, Iago told Othello _____ lies.

SYNONYMS: malicious, wicked, sinister, malignant
ANTONYMS: kind, benevolent, compassionate

13. nonchalant
(nän shə lant')

(*adj.*) cool and confident, unconcerned

The elegantly dressed couple strolled down the boulevard with a _____ air.

SYNONYMS: composed, unruffled, blasé
ANTONYMS: perturbed, agitated, disconcerted, abashed

14. omniscient
(äm nish′ ənt)

(*adj.*) knowing everything; having unlimited awareness or understanding

Scientists today have so much specialized knowledge that they sometimes seem _____.

SYNONYMS: wise, all-knowing
ANTONYMS: ignorant, unknowing

15. panacea
(pan ə sē′ ə)

(*n.*) a remedy for all ills; cure-all; an answer to all problems

You are mistaken if you think that getting more money will be a _____ for all your troubles.

SYNONYM: universal cure

16. scrupulous
(skrü′ pyə ləs)

(*adj.*) exact, careful, attending thoroughly to details; having high moral standards, principled

Scientists are trained to record their observations with _____ accuracy.

SYNONYMS: painstaking, meticulous, conscientious
ANTONYMS: careless, negligent, remiss, dishonest

17. skulk
(skəlk)

(*v.*) to move about stealthily; to lie in hiding

The burglar _____ in the alley looking for a way to get into the darkened jewelry store without attracting the attention of anyone who might be nearby.

SYNONYMS: lurk, slink, prowl

18. supercilious
(sü pər sil′ ē əs)

(*adj.*) proud and contemptuous; showing scorn because of a feeling of superiority

Their _____ attitude toward their servants was extremely offensive.

SYNONYMS: snobbish, patronizing, overbearing
ANTONYMS: humble, meek, deferential, servile

19. uncanny
(ən kan′ ē)

(*adj.*) strange, mysterious, weird, beyond explanation

It is highly unusual for a beginner to display such an _____ skill at playing bridge.

SYNONYMS: inexplicable, spooky

20. venial
(vē′ nē əl)

(*adj.*) easily excused; pardonable

Someone whose offense is deemed by the judge to be _____ may be ordered to perform community service.

SYNONYMS: excusable, forgivable
ANTONYMS: inexcusable, unforgivable, unpardonable

Choosing the Right Word

Select the **boldface** word that better completes each sentence. You might refer to the selection on pages 50–51 to see how most of these words are used in context.

1. Scientists have concluded that a sudden catastrophe (**expunged, converged**) dinosaurs from the face of the earth.

2. Instead of blaming a (**malevolent, invulnerable**) fate for your failures, why not look for the causes within yourself?

3. The critic recognized the book's faults but dismissed them as (**uncanny, venial**) in view of the author's overall achievement.

4. Instead of making an informed guess, why not (**ascertain, esteem**) exactly how many students are going on the trip to Washington?

5. Though the journey seemed interminable, I knew that it was (**cogent, finite**) and that I would soon be home.

6. When I splattered paint on my art teacher, I tried to appear (**nonchalant, malevolent**) but succeeded only in looking horrified.

Scientists have presented many hypotheses about the cause of the dinosaur extinction, including an asteroid collision with Earth.

7. Vast wealth, elegant clothes, and a (**finite, supercilious**) manner may make a snob, but they do not of themselves make a person a true gentleman or lady.

8. At first, the two candidates were in disagreement on every issue; but as the campaign went on, their opinions seemed to (**disperse, converge**).

9. When I found myself flushed with anger, I realized that I was not so (**scrupulous, invulnerable**) to their bitter sarcasm as I had thought I was!

10. Her bright, optimistic manner did much to (**ascertain, disperse**) the atmosphere of gloom that had settled over the meeting.

11. Lincoln said, "If you once forfeit the confidence of your fellow citizens, you can never regain their respect and (**esteem, attainment**)."

12. Though you forgot my birthday, and I did not receive a gift or card, it was a (**venial, scrupulous**) mistake and I shall forgive you.

13. When I walked into the abandoned house, I had this (**malevolent, uncanny**) feeling that someone was watching me.

14. Though the couple have spent years studying African history, they do not claim to be (**omniscient, cogent**) in that field.

15. We were overjoyed when we heard our university was going to invite an (**invulnerable, esteemed**) author and playwright to speak at our commencement.

16. It seems unimaginable that when I look at the night sky, the number of stars is actually (**finite, omniscient**).

17. There are so many different factors involved in an energy crisis that no single measure can be expected to serve as a(n) (**panacea, attainment**).

18. Nothing he may (**expunge, bequeath**) to the next generation can be more precious than the memory of his long life of honorable public service.

19. She is the kind of person who has many (**attainments, panaceas**) but seems unable to put them to any practical use.

20. The newspaper revealed that the city's chief building inspector was (**omniscient, affiliated**) with a large construction company.

21. Is it true that some dogs have a(n) (**uncanny, nonchalant**) sense of the approach of death?

22. I found your criticism of my conduct unpleasant, but I had to admit that your remarks were (**venial, cogent**).

23. The reform candidate vowed to root out the corruption that (**skulked, bequeathed**) through the corridors of City Hall.

24. As a member of the grand jury, it is your duty to be (**scrupulous, supercilious**) in weighing every bit of evidence.

25. A large crowd (**ascertained, converged**) on the mall to buy the latest gadget.

 **Synonyms** *Choose the word from this unit that is the same or most nearly the same in meaning as the **boldface** word or expression in the phrase. Write that word on the line. Use a dictionary if necessary.*

1. no **easy solution** for the problems of aging _____

2. an **eerie** tale of the supernatural _____

3. must **determine** who is responsible _____

4. **crept around** in the shadows of the old warehouse _____

5. **handed down** their knowledge to their apprentices _____

6. the **realization** of a cherished dream _____

7. a **quantifiable** amount of rainfall _____

8. an **indifferent** shrug of the shoulders _____

9. **resistant** to normal wear and tear _____

10. needed to **delete** out-of-date files _____

Antonyms

*Choose the word from this unit that is most nearly opposite in meaning to the **boldface** word or expression in the phrase. Write that word on the line. Use a dictionary if necessary.*

1. a **fretful** attitude _____

2. an **endless** supply of fresh water _____

3. an attempt to **create** a financial file _____

4. sought comfort in her **affliction** _____

5. a cat that **sped** across the lawn _____

Completing the Sentence

From the words in this unit, choose the one that best completes each of the following sentences. Write the word in the space provided.

1. When the candidate admitted openly that he had been mistaken in some of his earlier policies, we _____ him more highly than ever.

2. The screening committee investigated not only the candidates themselves but also the organizations with which they were _____.

3. So long as we remained indoors, we were _____ to the arctic blasts that swept down on our snowbound cabin.

4. Antibiotics were once considered wonder drugs, but we now know that they are not _____ for all our physical ailments.

5. I knew the dean would accept my apology when she characterized my behavior as thoughtless but _____.

6. Her election to Congress was the _____ of a lifelong ambition.

7. Though I wanted to "let bygones be bygones," I found that I could not wholly _____ the bitter memory of their behavior from my mind.

8. Before making our final plans, we should _____ exactly how much money we will have for expenses.

9. Your ability to guess what I am thinking about at any given time is nothing short of _____.

10. Because our natural resources are _____ and by no means inexhaustible, we must learn to conserve them.

11. In the opening scene of the horror film, a shadowy figure dressed in black
_____ through the graveyard in the moonlight.

12. The more knowledge and wisdom people acquire, the more keenly they become
aware that no one is _____.

13. Is there anyone in the world as _____ as a senior who attends a
mere sophomore class dance?

14. Only by paying _____ attention to innumerable details were the
investigators able to piece together the cause of the accident.

15. In a situation that would have left me all but helpless with embarrassment, he
remained cool and _____.

16. Isn't it remarkable how quickly a throng of sunbathers will pick up their belongings
and _____ when a few drops of rain fall?

17. If only parents could _____ their hard-won practical wisdom and
experience to their children!

18. When I saw the pain he caused others and the pleasure he took in doing so,
I realized he was a truly _____ person.

19. Our representative offered one simple but _____ argument
against the proposal: It would raise the cost of living.

20. As we stood on the railway tracks looking off into the distance, the rails seemed to
_____ and meet at some far-off point.

Writing: Words in Action

1. Look back at "Patronage of the Arts: Help or Hindrance?" (pages 50–51). Do
you believe that when an artist accepts a patron he or she sacrifices self-
expression in favor of the patron's taste? Does patronage support culture and
the arts or dictate it? Write a brief essay exploring these questions. Use at least
two details from the passage and three unit words to support your response.

2. Suppose you would like financial support for an intellectual, artistic, or social
endeavor. Perhaps you'd like to design a community center, compose music,
start a company, create a new computer application, or write and direct a film.
Write a letter of proposal to a prospective patron, attempting to persuade him
or her to support the project you have in mind. Present specific and
convincing reasons why your work is valuable and worth financing. Support
your proposal with specific examples from the reading (refer to pages 50–51)
and your own studies, observations, or personal experiences. Write at least
three paragraphs, and use three or more words from this unit.

Vocabulary in Context

Literary Text

The following excerpts are from Little Men *and* Little Women *by Louisa May Alcott. Some of the words you have studied in this unit appear in* **boldface** *type. Complete each statement below the excerpt by circling the letter of the correct answer.*

1. "My little John, I will be fair, and not pay a penny too much. Don't work too hard; and when that is done I will have something else for you to do," said Mrs. Jo, much touched by his desire to help, and his sense of justice, so like his **scrupulous** father. (*Little Men*)

    A **scrupulous** person is NOT

    a. honorable   **c.** reliable
    b. corrupt   **d.** sincere

2. He never spoke of himself, and no one ever knew that in his native city he had been a man much honored and **esteemed** for learning and integrity, till a countryman came to see him. (*Little Women*)

    To be **esteemed** by others is to be

    a. compensated   **c.** ostracized
    b. supported   **d.** admired

3. Poor Hannah was the first to recover, and with unconscious wisdom she set all the rest a good example, for with her, work was **panacea** for most afflictions. (*Little Women*)

    A **panacea** is a(n)

    a. obstacle   **c.** setback
    b. reason   **d.** cure-all

4. The latter informs the party that she **bequeaths** untold wealth to the young pair and an awful doom to Don Pedro, if he doesn't make them happy. (*Little Women*)

    A person who **bequeaths** wealth

    a. protects it   **c.** bestows it
    b. confiscates it **d.** utilizes it

Mariel Hemingway as Jo in the 1998 film version of *Little Men*.

5. "That's my favorite castle. What's yours, Meg?" Margaret seemed to find it a little hard to tell hers, and waved a brake before her face, as if to **disperse** imaginary gnats, while she said slowly, "I should like a lovely house, full of all sorts of luxurious things—nice food, pretty clothes, handsome furniture, pleasant people, and heaps of money." (*Little Women*)

    To **disperse** something is to

    a. scatter it   **c.** observe it
    b. count it   **d.** collect it

Interactive Quiz

Snap the code, or go to **vocabularyworkshop.com**

*Read the following selection, taking note of the **boldface** words and their contexts. These words are among those you will be studying in Unit 5. As you complete the exercises in this unit, it may help to refer to the way the words are used below.*

Democracy: From Athens to America

\<Speech\>

Lincoln at Gettysburg

As your student body president, it is my pleasure to address you during this celebration of the anniversary of Abraham Lincoln's Gettysburg Address. Lincoln spoke with **unfeigned** love for democracy when he delivered his magnificent speech. Today, we not only honor that momentous event, but also acknowledge the history behind it that reaches back over 3,000 years.

Lincoln's United States was a fledgling democracy—an experiment, really, or perhaps a stage in a long, **plodding** journey—that our forebears had boldly **embarked** upon. But in 1863, the country was divided by the Civil War. So when Lincoln stated that ours was a "government by the people, for the people," he expressed his **indomitable** belief in democracy.

What is democracy? It is a form of government in which political authority rests with the people and is conducted by and with their **assent**, or agreement. In a democracy, all citizens are entitled to equal opportunity and equality before the law. Furthermore, democracies are committed to the idea of majority rule. Although in practice democracy is not **infallible**, it is the most natural form of government we know. For as the ancient Greek philosopher Aristotle asserted, man is by nature a political animal.

The roots of our democracy go back to ancient Greek city-states. These entities were small, fortified, independent communities made up of a city and the surrounding countryside. Athens was the most populous—and the one where democracy first took hold. It was ruled by its citizens rather than by monarchs or aristocrats. But at a time when **diffident** and obedient populations ruled by tyrants or kings were the norm, democratic ideas

did not take hold overnight; rather, they emerged over time to the point we are at today in this country.

But democratic ideas did take hold eventually—after their early start some 2,600 years ago, when the aristocrat Draco gave Athens a written code of laws. These laws were harsh but clear, and though they favored the nobility, they became a foundation. Democratic ideas built on these laws a generation later, thanks to the **altruistic** and generous reformer Solon. He repealed many of Draco's harsh laws and replaced them with ones allowing for **clemency**. He also gave citizens a greater voice by establishing a lawmaking assembly. But it was under the leadership of Pericles that ancient democracy peaked and Athens entered its Golden Age. Pericles believed in citizen participation in government, and he had the **temerity** to give all citizens the right to criticize their leaders and generals. At a time when there was a **dearth** of individual rights, the forerunner of the modern democratic state had arrived. And with it came the first politicians, for Athenians prized the skills of oratory and persuasion.

While we must praise the Athenians for introducing democratic ideals to the world, we would be **remiss** not to recognize the **discrepancies** between their form of democracy and ours. Ours is a representative government, while theirs was a limited, direct form in which only

Solon of Athens

Athenian men participated. Indeed, only men who owned land were entitled to citizenship then. And only they could get an education or participate in cultural festivities. Women shared none of those rights. Neither did slaves, though they made up one-fourth of the population. That said, I believe it would be **facile** and insincere of me to condemn outright the shortcomings of the world's first democracy. Out of it developed the country that Abraham Lincoln was trying to unite and preserve on the day he dedicated a cemetery for the **repose** of the Civil War soldiers at Gettysburg. The gifts handed down to this country from ancient Greece and defended by our citizens and our leaders through the ages are something we should all cherish.

Reconstruction of Athens, Greece, at the time of Hadrian

iWords

Snap the code, or go to **vocabularyworkshop.com**

Definitions

Note the spelling, pronunciation, part(s) of speech, and definition(s) of each of the following words. Then write the word in the blank spaces in the illustrative sentence(s) following. Finally, study the lists of synonyms and antonyms.

1. altruistic
(al trü is' tik)

(*adj.*) unselfish, concerned with the welfare of others

Most people support _____ programs to help the less fortunate of this world.

SYNONYM: selfless
ANTONYMS: selfish, self-centered

2. assent
(ə sent')

(*v.*) to express agreement; (*n.*) agreement

Workers hope that the threat of a long strike will force management to _____ to their demands. Romeo and Juliet knew they would never gain their feuding families' _____ to marry.

SYNONYMS: (*v.*) consent, concur
ANTONYMS: (*v.*) disagree, differ, dissent

3. benefactor
(ben' ə fak tər)

(*n.*) one who does good to others

Without the help of many _____, most charities would be unable to carry out their work.

SYNONYMS: patron, humanitarian
ANTONYMS: misanthrope, malefactor

4. chivalrous
(shiv' əl rəs)

(*adj.*) marked by honor, courtesy, and courage; knightly

In today's busy world, where people are often heedless of others, a _____ act is admired by all.

SYNONYMS: civil, valiant, courtly
ANTONYMS: uncouth, churlish, loutish

5. clemency
(klem' ən sē)

(*n.*) mercy, humaneness; mildness, moderateness

Many judges are willing to show _____ to first offenders who express regret for their wrongdoing.

SYNONYMS: leniency, forbearance, gentleness
ANTONYMS: harshness, severity, cruelty, inflexibility

6. dearth
(dərth)

(*n.*) a lack, scarcity, inadequate supply; a famine

An employer may complain of a _____ of qualified applicants for available jobs.

SYNONYMS: insufficiency, want, paucity
ANTONYMS: surplus, oversupply, glut, abundance

7. diffident
(dif′ ə dənt)

(*adj.*) shy, lacking self-confidence; modest, reserved

Many a _____ suitor has lost his beloved to a bold rival.

SYNONYMS: timid, bashful, unassertive, withdrawn
ANTONYMS: bold, brash, audacious, self-confident, jaunty

8. discrepancy
(dis krep′ ən sē)

(*n.*) a difference; a lack of agreement

_____ in the testimony of witnesses to a crime can have a decisive impact on the outcome of a trial.

SYNONYMS: disagreement, divergence, inconsistency
ANTONYMS: agreement, convergence, consistency

9. embark
(em bärk′)

(*v.*) to go aboard; to make a start; to invest

Columbus spent years raising money before he was able to _____ on his perilous ocean voyage in search of a passage to the Far East.

SYNONYMS: commence, begin, board

10. facile
(fas′ əl)

(*adj.*) easily done or attained; superficial; ready, fluent; easily shown but not sincerely felt

Writing is a _____ process for some authors but a laborious task for others.

SYNONYMS: effortless, assured, poised, specious
ANTONYMS: labored, awkward, halting

11. indomitable
(in däm′ ət ə bəl)

(*adj.*) unconquerable, refusing to yield

All who hear of the remarkable deeds of Harriet Tubman admire her _____ courage in the face of grave danger.

SYNONYMS: unbeatable, invincible, unyielding
ANTONYMS: surrendering, submissive, yielding

12. infallible
(in fal′ ə bəl)

(*adj.*) free from error; absolutely dependable

Some critics seem convinced that their expert knowledge makes them _____ judges of the quality of an artist's work.

SYNONYMS: unerring, certain
ANTONYM: imperfect

13. plod
(pläd)

(*v.*) to walk heavily or slowly; to work slowly

After the blizzard, we had to _____ through deep snowdrifts to reach the nearest stores.

SYNONYMS: lumber, trudge
ANTONYMS: scamper, skip, prance

14. pungent
(pən' jənt)

(*adj.*) causing a sharp sensation; stinging, biting
The kitchen of the French restaurant was filled with the
_____ aroma of onion soup.

SYNONYMS: sharp, spicy, piquant, racy
ANTONYMS: unappetizing, colorless, insipid

15. remiss
(rē mis')

(*adj.*) neglectful in performance of one's duty, careless
When I am _____ in doing daily chores, I
have to spend a big part of the weekend catching up.

SYNONYMS: negligent, lax, slack
ANTONYMS: scrupulous, dutiful, punctilious

16. repose
(rē pōz')

(*v.*) to rest; lie; place; (*n.*) relaxation, peace of mind, calmness
The mortal remains of thousands who fell in America's wars
_____ in Arlington National Cemetery.

After spending all day with others, you may wish for a period
of _____ before dinner.

SYNONYMS: (*v.*) sleep; (*n.*) tranquility, respite
ANTONYMS: (*n.*) exertion, wakefulness, tumult, bustle, ado

17. temerity
(tə mer' ə tē)

(*n.*) rashness, boldness
Few of his subordinates had the _____ to
answer the general back.

SYNONYMS: recklessness, foolhardiness, effrontery
ANTONYMS: timidity, fearfulness, diffidence, humility

18. truculent
(trək' yə lənt)

(*adj.*) fierce and cruel; aggressive; deadly, destructive;
scathingly harsh
People with _____ dispositions can make
life miserable for those who have to work with them.

SYNONYMS: savage, belligerent, vitriolic
ANTONYMS: gentle, mild, unthreatening

19. unfeigned
(ən fānd')

(*adj.*) sincere, real, without pretense
The novelist won high praise for her ability to portray the
_____ emotions of children.

SYNONYMS: genuine, heartfelt
ANTONYMS: insincere, simulated, phony

20. virulent
(vir' yə lənt)

(*adj.*) extremely poisonous; full of malice; spiteful
The First Amendment protects the right of free speech for
everyone, even those with _____ views
that are repugnant to most people.

SYNONYMS: noxious, baneful, hateful
ANTONYMS: harmless, benign

Choosing the Right Word

Select the **boldface** word that better completes each sentence. You might refer to the selection on pages 60–61 to see how most of these words are used in context.

1. By 1781, George Washington's green recruits of a few years earlier had been forged into an (**infallible, indomitable**) army.

2. How do you account for the (**clemency, dearth**) of doctors who are general practitioners rather than specialists?

3. She is a popular young woman because people realize that her interest in them is sympathetic and (**remiss, unfeigned**).

George Washington crossed the Delaware River with his troops.

4. After boasting to me of your family's great wealth, how could you have the (**clemency, temerity**) to ask me for a loan?

5. After the hurricane destroyed the city, the people of New Orleans showed their (**diffident, indomitable**) spirit by rebuilding.

6. The recipe for my great-grandfather's spaghetti sauce, (**pungent, facile**) with bay leaves and other herbs, has been passed down for several generations.

7. I had no inkling of your deep-seated aversion to pop music until I overheard your (**altruistic, virulent**) comments about it.

8. Caring nothing about negative repercussions, Katy had the (**temerity, discrepancy**) to ask not only for a raise but also for a more flexible schedule.

9. You will surely win more support for your view by quiet discussion than by (**truculent, chivalrous**) attacks on your opponents.

10. Planet Earth is a sort of spaceship on which billions of human beings have (**reposed, embarked**) on a lifelong voyage.

11. With all the deductions for taxes, there is a substantial (**dearth, discrepancy**) between my official salary and my weekly paycheck.

12. The critic's (**pungent, facile**) comments during the TV panel show were not only amusing but also very much to the point.

13. I admired the speaker's (**remiss, facile**) flow of words, but they failed to convince me that she had practical ideas to help solve our problems.

14. We breathed a sigh of relief when we saw the supposedly missing set of keys (**plodding, reposing**) in the desk drawer.

15. We soon learned that behind his retiring and (**truculent, diffident**) manner, there is a keen mind and a strong will.

16. In the violent world of today's pro football, good sportsmanship and (**chivalrous, pungent**) behavior still have a place.

17. Given the glaring (**benefactors, discrepancies**) between the applicant's résumé and his actual experience, he did not receive the job.

18. American Presidents often point to one of their schoolteachers as the (**discrepancy, benefactor**) who helped shape their character and ideas.

19. He is not too well informed on most matters; but when it comes to big-league baseball, he is all but (**indomitable, infallible**).

20. As a state legislator, you should not give your (**assent, chivalry**) to any measure unless you truly believe in it.

21. Great political leaders know how to appeal to people not only through self-interest but also through their sense of (**temerity, altruism**).

22. The lawyer (**plodded, embarked**) through hundreds of pages of the trial record, hoping to find some basis for an appeal.

23. In a grim old joke, a man found guilty of murdering his parents appeals for (**clemency, assent**) because he is an orphan.

24. It would be (**remiss, indomitable**) of me, as editor-in-chief of the school newspaper, not to express appreciation for the help of our faculty advisor.

25. I enjoy reading stories about King Arthur and his (**chivalrous, virulent**) knights.

Synonyms

*Choose the word from this unit that is the same or most nearly the same in meaning as the **boldface** word or expression in the phrase. Write that word on the line. Use a dictionary if necessary.*

1. gallant actions are not a thing of the past _____

2. start on a new endeavor in his life _____

3. generous **sponsors** of the foundation _____

4. found **serenity** in the shade of a tree _____

5. refused to **accede** to the will of the majority _____

6. humanitarian dedication to finding a cure _____

7. a **caustic** response to a hostile question _____

8. a **brutal** band of hardened criminals _____

9. made allowances for the **audacity** of youth _____

10. the spreading of **venomous** rumors _____

Antonyms

*Choose the word from this unit that is most nearly opposite in meaning to the **boldface** word or expression in the phrase. Write that word on the line. Use a dictionary if necessary.*

1. made a **crude** apology for his behavior _____

2. an extremely **bland** spice _____

3. making a **meek** observation about taxes _____

4. wrote an **innocuous** letter to the person in charge _____

5. discovered the identity of the **detractor** _____

Completing the Sentence

From the words in this unit, choose the one that best completes each of the following sentences. Write the word in the space provided.

1. We were all impressed by your _____ use of unusual words and expressions that you had learned only a few hours before.

2. It was quite _____ of you to give up your seat so that the man with the cane did not have to stand during the bus trip.

3. Your _____ joy when it was announced that I had won the scholarship meant more to me than all the polite congratulations I received.

4. Doctors attributed the epidemic to the rampant spread of a particularly _____ strain of influenza virus.

5. I rarely join in the discussions because I am _____.

6. History tells us that many men and women regarded as failures in their own lifetimes were actually major _____ of humanity.

7. Humor should be clever and amusing but never so _____ that it hurts the feelings of other people.

8. The exhausted refugees _____ along the dusty road, hoping to reach the Red Cross camp before nightfall.

9. As soon as the last passenger had _____, the captain ordered the ship to get under way.

10. The rash young lieutenant had the _____ to disregard the express orders of the commanding officer.

11. The custom of putting erasers on pencils is one way of recognizing the fact that no one is _____.

12. My parents will not _____ to my going to the dance unless I promise faithfully to be home no later than 1:00 A.M.

13. Refusing to admit defeat even when things looked completely hopeless, our _____ football team drove eighty-five yards in the last few minutes to score the winning touchdown.

14. In view of the many able people in public life today, I do not agree that we are suffering from a(n) _____ of capable leaders.

15. Emphasizing the youth of the convicted man, the defense attorney pleaded for _____.

16. The principal claimed that there were major _____ between what actually happened in the school and the way the incident was reported on TV.

17. He is not merely unpleasant but actually dangerous whenever he gets into one of his _____ moods.

18. As a school cafeteria guard, I would be _____ in my duties if I failed to report a serious disturbance.

19. What good are _____ principles if no real attempt is made to help people by putting those principles into practice?

20. I did not realize how beautiful the twins were until they fell asleep and I saw their faces in complete _____.

Writing: Words in Action

1. Look back at "Democracy: From Athens to America" (pages 60–61). In a brief essay, identify the main tenets, or principles, of democracy. Explain how these principles continue to influence life in the United States today. Use at least two details from the passage and three unit words to support your analysis.

2. *"Our liberty depends on the freedom of the press, and that cannot be limited without being lost." —Thomas Jefferson*

Do you agree or disagree with Thomas Jefferson's statement? In a brief essay, paraphrase what Jefferson is saying, and support your opinion of his statement with specific examples from your observations, studies, reading (refer to pages 60–61), or personal experiences. Write at least three paragraphs, and use three or more words from this unit.

Vocabulary in Context

The following excerpts are from the novel My Antonia *by Willa Cather. Some of the words you have studied in this unit appear in* **boldface** *type. Complete each statement below the excerpt by circling the letter of the correct answer.*

1. Grandmother looked anxiously at grandfather. He took off his hat, and the other men did likewise. I thought his prayer remarkable. I still remember it.... He prayed that if any man there had been **remiss** toward the stranger come to a far country, God would forgive him and soften his heart.

To be **remiss** is to be

a. ambitious
b. courteous
c. inoffensive
d. thoughtless

2. I loved the dim superstition, the propitiatory intent, that had put the grave there; and still more I loved the spirit that could not carry out the sentence—the error from the surveyed lines, the **clemency** of the soft earth roads along which the home-coming wagons rattled after sunset.

If a road seems to have **clemency**, it is

a. paved
b. winding
c. smooth
d. bumpy

3. Julia was in the hammock—she was fond of **repose**—and Frances was at the piano, playing without a light and talking to her mother through the open window.

A person who enjoys **repose** likes to

a. relax
b. gossip
c. sway
d. sing

4. Why had Coronado never gone back to Spain, to his riches and his castles and his king? I couldn't tell them. I only knew the schoolbooks said he "died in the wilderness, of a broken heart."

"More than him has done that," said Antonia sadly, and the girls murmured **assent**.

Willa Cather's novels, often about frontier life on the Great Plains, feature strong female characters.

To show **assent** is to show

a. humility
b. confusion
c. opposition
d. accord

5. When Mrs. Shimerda opened the bag and stirred the contents with her hand, it gave out a salty, earthy smell, very **pungent**, even among the other odors of that cave.

A **pungent** odor is NOT

a. musky
b. mild
c. rich
d. strong

Snap the code, or go to **vocabularyworkshop.com**

Read the following selection, taking note of the **boldface** words and their contexts. These words are among those you will be studying in Unit 6. As you complete the exercises in this unit, it may help to refer to the way the words are used below.

When the Wall Came Tumbling Down
<Oral History>

The Brandenberg Gate behind the Berlin Wall

My grandparents' generation came of age in a divided country. In 1961, East Germany's Communist government built the Berlin Wall, which divided the city in two. The construction of this wall was a **premeditated** act, planned by a vengeful regime determined to **brandish** its power in the decades following the Allied victory over Hitler's Germany. My grandmother said isolating West Berlin from the rest of Soviet-controlled East Germany was a way for the regime to thumb its nose at Western democracies. In a **deft** statement of double-speak, East Germany's leaders claimed that the wall would shelter its people from "the ravages of capitalism." Even if the wall's real purpose had not been made **explicit** already, the truth was soon obvious to all: It prevented East Germans like my grandparents from fleeing to West Germany in search of freedom and a better life.

By the time I was born, that ugly concrete wall, with its **ominous** watchtowers, was a daily reminder of East German control and repression. Rather than protect us, the Berlin Wall was a cruel blockade that cost nearly 300 people their lives. Some tried to climb or fly over it, and others tried to dig under or around it, but most failed in their attempts to breach that barrier. They were all trying to escape a country in which everyday life was marked by our political leaders' **officious** rules. Every law was rigidly enforced by the **venal** secret police. We both despised and feared them.

Despite our fears, despite the guards, it was regular people like me who finally brought down the wall simply by walking through its checkpoints. **Ironic**, isn't it? What happened was this. During the late 1980s, the East German government gradually became less rigid. Bit by bit, it began offering its people more freedoms. Then in 1989, its leaders declared that on November 9, anyone who had a proper visa could visit West Germany. I did not have a visa, but I went to the wall anyway with some friends. Within hours, the crowd had become huge, and it was clear that the guards were overwhelmed. They could no longer keep back the thousands and thousands of people who wanted to pass through the checkpoints.

I'm not sure if it was that the guards were outnumbered and scared, or that they, too, wanted freedom. But suddenly, the barricades were open, and when people began to walk through, the guards let them. That's really when the wall came down. We did not physically tear it apart, brick by brick. But it was clear the wall no longer served as a threat or a barricade. In our minds, it was already gone.

Above: The scene as the wall fell in November 1989

I will never forget what it was like to be in Berlin that November. Everywhere in the streets people were dancing and laughing. You could hear horns and music from one end of the city to the other. I saw people spray-painting democratic slogans on the wall and even hammering off chunks to keep as souvenirs. Everyone was smiling and laughing—it was an amazing contrast to the gloom I used to feel when walking past the wall as a kid.

On November 10, my friend Anja and I went to the **stately** Brandenburg Gate, the centuries-old symbol of Berlin that had been cut in two by the wall. People were still gathering in the streets, still dancing, still laughing. We were all celebrating freedom, something most of us probably never thought we would experience. Suddenly, as Anja and I were dancing, an armed soldier left his post by the wall and walked toward us. That made Anja and me nervous. He reached out to shake our hands. Then he and I swapped caps. We each had a huge smile on our face—I swear, it was the **pinnacle** of our lives, the happiest day ever! Imagine the **solace** that comes from realizing that in just 24 hours, we had gone from being enemies to being friends.

Although joy was **rampant** and evident in everyone's eyes, within days, our delight was muted by concerns about what was ahead for our country. We were no longer trapped behind the wall, but we had lived for generations under a harsh regime. To get by, East Germans had learned to **suppress** their hopes and dreams. Citizens had to **accede** to the rules of the communist system, or face prison—or worse. Now that the wall was down and our government was weakened, how would we **extirpate** the fears and anxieties that had plagued our lives? These were the questions people asked in the days and weeks after the Berlin Wall fell. But during those glorious first days, all we knew was that we were making history— and that soon, the two Germanys would be reunited as a single nation.

Snap the code, or go to
vocabularyworkshop.com

Definitions

Note the spelling, pronunciation, part(s) of speech, and definition(s) of each of the following words. Then write the word in the blank spaces in the illustrative sentence(s) following. Finally, study the lists of synonyms and antonyms.

1. accede
(ak sēd')

(*v.*) to yield to; to assume an office or dignity

Management was not willing to _____ to labor's initial demands, thus increasing the likelihood of a long and bitter strike.

SYNONYMS: consent, concur, comply, assent
ANTONYMS: demur, balk at

2. brandish
(bran' dish)

(*v.*) to wave or flourish in a menacing or vigorous fashion

I _____ my umbrella repeatedly in a vain effort to hail a cab.

SYNONYMS: swing, shake

3. comprise
(kəm prīz')

(*v.*) to include or contain; to be made up of

Classical symphonies usually _____ three or four movements of varying musical form, tempo, and character.

SYNONYMS: compose, constitute, encompass
ANTONYM: exclude

4. deft
(deft)

(*adj.*) skillful, nimble

The _____ fingers of Spanish seamstresses produced some of the finest, most delicate lace ever seen.

SYNONYMS: dexterous, adroit, proficient, clever, masterful
ANTONYMS: clumsy, awkward, bungling, inept

5. destitute
(des' tə tüt)

(*adj.*) deprived of the necessities of life; lacking in

Some people fled their homes so suddenly that they arrived at the refugee camp absolutely _____.

SYNONYMS: wanting, devoid, penniless
ANTONYMS: rich, luxurious, bountiful, full, replete

6. explicit
(ek splis' it)

(*adj.*) definite, clearly stated

The more _____ your directions are, the easier it will be for all of us to find our way to the campsite.

SYNONYMS: distinct, forthright, unambiguous, clear
ANTONYMS: vague, ambiguous, implied, implicit

7. extirpate
(ek′ stər pāt)

(*v.*) to tear up by the roots; to destroy totally

We must do everything we can to _____ racism from American society.

SYNONYMS: uproot, eradicate, wipe out, excise
ANTONYMS: implant, sow, foster, nourish

8. inopportune
(in äp ər tün′)

(*adj.*) coming at a bad time; not appropriate

Why do my relatives always seem to turn up at the most _____ time imaginable?

SYNONYMS: ill-timed, inconvenient, inappropriate, unsuitable
ANTONYMS: timely, convenient, felicitous, opportune

9. ironic
(ī rän′ ik)

(*adj.*) suggesting an incongruity between what might be expected and what actually happens; given to irony, sarcastic

The short stories of O. Henry are famous for their _____ endings.

SYNONYMS: incongruous, satiric, sardonic, wry
ANTONYMS: straightforward, unequivocal

10. musty
(məs′ tē)

(*adj.*) stale, moldy; out-of-date

Houses that have been closed up for a very long time often have an unpleasantly _____ smell about them.

SYNONYMS: hackneyed, antiquated
ANTONYMS: sweet-smelling, up-to-date, brand-new

11. officious
(ə fish′ əs)

(*adj.*) meddling; excessively forward in offering services or assuming authority

The manager of the store warned the entire sales force not to be too _____ when helping customers.

SYNONYMS: meddlesome, prying, impertinent, obtrusive
ANTONYMS: reserved, diffident, timid, aloof

12. ominous
(äm′ ən əs)

(*adj.*) unfavorable, threatening, of bad omen

The _____ sound of distant thunder warned us of the storm's approach.

SYNONYMS: unpropitious, inauspicious, portentous
ANTONYMS: propitious, auspicious, promising

13. pinnacle
(pin′ ə kəl)

(*n.*) a high peak or point

Some pop musicians reach the _____ of their careers comparatively early in life.

SYNONYMS: apex, acme, summit, apogee
ANTONYMS: nadir, perigee, low point

14. **premeditated**
(prē med′ ə tāt id)

(*adj., part.*) considered beforehand, deliberately planned

Some crimes are spontaneous acts of passion; others are quite _____.

SYNONYMS: preplanned, rehearsed, prearranged
ANTONYMS: unplanned, spontaneous, impromptu

15. **rampant**
(ram′ pənt)

(*adj.*) growing without check, running wild

All kinds of odd rumors run _____ during a political campaign.

SYNONYMS: widespread, unrestrained, extravagant, prevalent
ANTONYMS: controlled, restrained

16. **solace**
(säl′ əs)

(*n.*) comfort, relief; (*v.*) to comfort, console

Many world leaders seek _____ from the cares of state in the pages of great literature.

I could find no way to _____ my deeply troubled conscience.

SYNONYMS: (*v.*) soothe, reassure, cheer up
ANTONYMS: (*v.*) vex, aggravate, upset

17. **stately**
(stāt′ lē)

(*adj.*) dignified, majestic

The _____ procession slowly wound its way from the palace to the cathedral.

SYNONYMS: grand, magnificent, imposing
ANTONYMS: lowly, humble, servile, abject

18. **supple**
(səp′ əl)

(*adj.*) bending easily; bending with agility; readily adaptable; servile

Have you ever read Robert Frost's famous poem about swinging on the _____ branches of a birch tree?

SYNONYMS: flexible, limber, pliable, pliant
ANTONYMS: rigid, unbending, hidebound

19. **suppress**
(sə pres′)

(*v.*) to stop by force, put down

Totalitarian governments usually take strong measures to _____ free speech.

SYNONYMS: subdue, crush, stifle, squelch, quash, silence
ANTONYMS: provoke, spur, arouse, incite, instigate

20. **venal**
(vēn′ əl)

(*adj.*) open to or marked by bribery or corruption

The presence of even one _____ official may jeopardize the integrity of an entire organization.

SYNONYMS: dishonest, bribable, corruptible, mercenary
ANTONYMS: honest, incorruptible, scrupulous

Choosing the Right Word

Select the **boldface** word that better completes each sentence. You might refer to the essay on pages 70–71 to see how most of these words are used in context.

1. Eliza Doolittle was a poor flower seller, but she learned to conduct herself with the (**supple, stately**) bearing of a princess.

2. Coming at a time when I was flat broke, your suggestion that we have a bite to eat and go to the movies was highly (**officious, inopportune**).

3. Was Oscar Wilde being (**ironic, deft**) when he said that he could resist everything except temptation?

4. The way he (**brandishes, comprises**) his facts and figures reminds me of a butcher swinging a meat cleaver.

5. Someone who believes that everyone has a price must think that human beings are (**premeditated, venal**) by nature.

Audrey Hepburn played Eliza Doolittle in the 1964 film *My Fair Lady,* based on the play *Pygmalion* by George Bernard Shaw.

6. Traveling in the dead of night, the weary travelers found (**solace, pinnacle**) knowing that their journey would lead them to freedom.

7. He is in for a rude awakening if he thinks that as the son of a rich family, he will simply (**suppress, accede**) to a position of wealth and power.

8. There's a world of difference between a helpful research assistant and an (**explicit, officious**) one!

9. Even in the prisoner-of-war camps, some basic feelings of decency and humanity were not completely (**brandished, extirpated**).

10. I have no patience with (**musty, stately**) old ideas about family roles based on gender.

11. His speech at first seemed highly dramatic and impressive, but we soon realized that he was quite (**destitute, musty**) of new ideas.

12. She has the kind of (**supple, venal**) personality that can easily adapt itself to a wide variety of needs and conditions.

13. Let's prepare a joint statement that will (**accede, comprise**) the various objections of all civic groups to the freeway plan.

14. How unfortunate that those in power are often presumed to have a(n) (**venal, inopportune**) nature.

15. The only sure way to (**brandish, suppress**) social unrest is to make possible a decent, secure life for all the people.

16. During the darkest hours of defeat, their only (**solace, pinnacle**) was the knowledge that they had fought hard to the very end.

17. (**Extirpating, Comprising**) everything in its path, the deadly tornado left nothing but a desolate landscape.

18. The actress felt that she had reached the (**solace, pinnacle**) of fame when the principal of her former school asked for her autograph.

19. The senator finally (**brandished, acceded**) to the controversial legislation, handing her opponents a victory.

20. They tried to explain away their insult as a slip of the tongue, but in my opinion it was deliberate and (**premeditated, ominous**).

21. No doubt there are some dishonest officials, but it is a gross exaggeration to say that graft and corruption are (**rampant, explicit**) in our government.

22. We were prepared for a sharp scolding but not for the (**inopportune, ominous**) silence with which the principal greeted us.

23. No matter how ticklish the situation, the hero of the cartoon always devised some (**deft, rampant**) maneuver to avoid capture.

24. If the law is intended to limit nonessential use of gasoline and heating oil, it should state this (**ironically, explicitly**).

25. If you need to (**accede, suppress**) an itching rash, try an herbal remedy.

 **Synonyms**

*Choose the word from this unit that is the same or most nearly the same in meaning as the **boldface** word or expression in the phrase. Write that word on the line. Use a dictionary if necessary.*

1. the **distinguished** language of the Gettysburg Address _____

2. a **stuffy** old office building _____

3. **consists of** bits and pieces of longer works _____

4. a **contradictory** conclusion to a promising career _____

5. left the orphans totally **impoverished** _____

6. at the very **height** of the social scene _____

7. a rule that is **adjustable** if circumstances require _____

8. actions that were obviously **calculated** _____

9. annoyingly **intrusive** coworkers _____

10. an **unseemly** occasion for a feast _____

Antonyms

*Choose the word from this unit that is most nearly opposite in meaning to the **boldface** word or expression in the phrase. Write that word on the line. Use a dictionary if necessary.*

1. a **fresh-smelling** box of books _____

2. sections of the city that are extremely **wealthy** _____

3. a most **fitting** time to visit _____

4. an extremely **stiff** fabric _____

5. an art collection that **omits** important works _____

Completing the Sentence

From the words in this unit, choose the one that best completes each of the following sentences. Write the word in the space provided.

1. I vowed that I would _____ every weed that dared to show itself in our newly seeded lawn.

2. The sudden drop in temperature and the unnatural stillness in the air were _____ signs of an unfavorable change in the weather.

3. "We could not have chosen a more _____ spot for our picnic," she observed as she swept ants off the blanket.

4. The referee gave a(n) _____ warning that if either team protested her decisions, she would be forced to call a technical foul.

5. Accomplished portrait painters can usually reveal a person's character with a few _____ strokes of a brush.

6. A great dancer, like a great athlete, must have a sharp sense of timing and a highly trained, responsive, and _____ body.

7. Even when the economy is strong, there are always a large number of _____ families in urgent need of assistance.

8. We will never _____ to those selfish and unfair terms.

9. It is a sobering thought to realize that when one has reached the _____ of a mountain, there is nowhere to go but down.

10. Airline companies often call in professional grief counselors to help _____ the families and friends of crash victims.

11. How _____ that they finally inherited all that money at a time when it could no longer help to solve their problems!

12. The unruly mob retreated as the line of deputies moved forward slowly, _____ their riot sticks.

13. How can I ever forget that _____ inspector in the customs office who insisted that I empty every piece of luggage before him!

14. The students couldn't _____ their groans of dismay when the teacher announced a surprise quiz.

15. Unfortunately, the so-called recreational facilities _____ nothing more than a card table and a small-screen TV set.

16. Attacking the present administration, the candidate said that crime has been _____ in the streets of our city.

17. Who can forget the stirring sight of those _____ tall ships with their lofty masts and graceful lines as they sailed past the Statue of Liberty on the Fourth of July?

18. Who would have dreamed that the cluttered old attic, with all its darkness, dust, and _____ odor, contained such a treasure!

19. Whether your act was _____ or the result of carelessness, the fact remains that you have caused great pain to someone who has always been very good to you.

20. In the mid-1800s, "Boss" Tweed controlled New York City through a(n) _____ political machine that fed on graft and extortion.

Writing: Words in Action

1. Look back at "When the Wall Came Tumbling Down" (pages 70–71). Imagine that you are an American visiting Berlin in 1989 when the wall falls. Write a newspaper article for your local paper reporting what you saw, heard, felt, and learned during the experience. Use vivid descriptions and include a quoted statement from at least one German citizen. Conclude your article with an observation about the symbolic importance of the fall of the wall. Use at least two details from the passage and three unit words to support your insight.

2. The Berlin Wall was not only a physical barrier, dividing East Germany from West Germany, but it was also a symbolic obstruction, keeping many people from freedom. In a short essay, describe another wall (either real or symbolic) that continues to limit people's freedoms, and explore this question: What can make that wall "come tumbling down"? Use examples from the reading (pages 70–71), as well as your own observations, studies, or personal knowledge. Write at least three paragraphs, and use three or more words from this unit.

Vocabulary in Context

Literary Text

The following excerpts are from Wuthering Heights *by Emily Brontë. Some of the words you have studied in this unit appear in **boldface** type. Complete each statement below the excerpt by circling the letter of the correct answer.*

1. I saw him smile to himself—grin rather—and lapse into **ominous** musing whenever Mrs. Linton had occasion to be absent from the apartment.

   Thoughts that are **ominous** are NOT

   a. gloomy   **c.** hopeful
   b. dismal   **d.** harmful

2. Linton looked at me, but did not answer; and, after keeping her seat by his side another ten minutes, during which his head fell drowsily on his breast, and he uttered nothing except suppressed moans of exhaustion or pain, Cathy began to seek **solace** in looking for bilberries, and sharing the produce of her researches with me: she did not offer them to him, for she saw further notice would only weary and annoy.

   To seek **solace** is to seek

   a. respite   **c.** amusement
   b. defeat   **d.** danger

3. It was a Testament, in lean type, and smelling dreadfully **musty**: a fly-leaf bore the inscription—"Catherine Earnshaw, her book," and a date some quarter of a century back.

   A book that has a **musty** smell is most likely

   a. new   **c.** old
   b. rare   **d.** original

Laurence Olivier plays Heathcliff and Merle Oberon plays Catherine in the classic 1939 film adaptation of *Wuthering Heights*.

4. The lands, being a minor, he could not meddle with. However, Mr. Heathcliff has claimed and kept them in his wife's right and his also: I suppose legally; at any rate, Catherine, **destitute** of cash and friends, cannot disturb his possession.

   Someone who is **destitute** is

   a. vigilant   **c.** prosperous
   b. needy   **d.** proficient

5. "...Time stagnates here: we must surely have retired to rest at eight!"

   "Always at nine in winter, and rise at four," said my host, **suppressing** a groan: and, as I fancied, by the motion of his arm's shadow, dashing a tear from his eyes.

   The act of **suppressing** involves

   a. changing   **c.** conveying
   b. consoling   **d.** restraining

Interactive Quiz

Snap the code, or go to
vocabularyworkshop.com

Vocabulary for Comprehension

*Read the following selection in which some of the words you have studied in Units 4–6 appear in **boldface** type. Then answer the questions on page 81.*

The following passage describes an easy way to attract butterflies and contribute to their conservation.

(Line)

Butterfly populations are on the decline around the world, mainly because of the loss of habitat and the use of pesticides. But there is

(5) something you can do right in your own backyard to help reverse this trend. With a little time and effort, you can create a welcoming environment in which these beautiful

(10) creatures can find food and lay their eggs in safety.

Your first step is to **ascertain** which species of flowers attract the butterflies that are native to your

(15) area. These insects are drawn to brightly colored, nectar-rich flowers that have a strong scent. Butterflies see more color than humans do, and they have a finely tuned sense of

(20) smell. They are said to be able to identify their favorite plants from miles away. They also need trees, shrubs, and leafy green plants on which to lay their eggs and on which

(25) hatched caterpillars can feed.

Next, you will want to give some thought to the arrangement of the shrubs and flowers you plant. For example, **stately** trees and shrubs

(30) such as cottonwood, tulip poplar, lantana, privet, and hibiscus may be

combined with shorter, more **supple** flowering plants such as bee balm, borage, and lavender to provide

(35) protection as well as food.

An abundance of varied types of flowering plants is the best possible butterfly magnet you can use. But you need not be **scrupulous** about

(40) separating flowers into isolated, symmetrical beds of similar species or colors. Nor do you need to work as hard as other gardeners to **suppress** weeds and wildflowers.

(45) Even crabgrass provides food for some species of caterpillars.

Butterflies cannot regulate their own body temperatures, so be sure to plant your garden in a sunny spot.

(50) Include some rocks or other exposed surfaces on which butterflies can **repose** with wings outstretched to soak up the sun. Butterflies can also benefit from

(55) windbreaks and sheltered places where they can hide from the elements and sleep at night.

1. The main purpose of the passage is to
   a. describe the breeding of butterflies
   b. give directions for butterfly gardening
   c. discuss the benefits of butterfly conservation
   d. provide resources for studying butterflies
   e. describe the joys of butterfly watching

2. In the first paragraph (lines 1–11), the author provides a rationale for
   a. weeding the backyard
   b. watching butterflies
   c. using pesticides
   d. creating a butterfly habitat
   e. starting a new trend

3. Paragraph 2 (lines 12–25) focuses on
   a. plant selection
   b. gardening techniques
   c. garden location
   d. flower arrangement
   e. garden maintenance

4. The meaning of **ascertain** (line 12) is
   a. memorize
   b. acquire
   c. eliminate
   d. describe
   e. discover

5. **Stately** (line 29) most nearly means
   a. rare
   b. slender
   c. imposing
   d. modest
   e. colorful

6. **Supple** (line 32) is best defined as
   a. statuesque
   b. limber
   c. exotic
   d. costly
   e. commonplace

7. The meaning of **scrupulous** (line 39) is
   a. timid
   b. honest
   c. relaxed
   d. painstaking
   e. excited

8. **Suppress** (line 44) most nearly means
   a. promote
   b. irrigate
   c. spread
   d. avoid
   e. stifle

9. **Repose** (line 52) is best defined as
   a. tranquility
   b. display
   c. signal
   d. rest
   e. flutter

10. To attract butterflies, you need to provide all of the following EXCEPT
    a. flower beds of one species
    b. sheltered areas for protection
    c. nectar plants for adults
    d. sunny places for resting
    e. food plants for caterpillars

11. Based on the passage, which of the following generalizations is true?
    a. Butterfly gardens have restored declining butterfly populations.
    b. Butterfly gardens do not require planning.
    c. Butterfly gardens contribute to the conservation of butterflies.
    d. Butterfly gardens are on the decline around the world.
    e. Butterfly gardens must be carefully tended.

12. The author of the passage would probably agree with which of the following statements?
    a. A garden does not have to be colorful to attract butterflies.
    b. A garden does not have to be well manicured to be attractive.
    c. Butterfly watching is better than bird watching.
    d. Only an experienced gardener should attempt butterfly gardening.
    e. Butterfly gardening is worthwhile only if you enjoy butterfly watching.

Two-Word Completions

Select the pair of words that best complete the meaning of each of the following passages.

1. Pundits were quick to note the _____ when the councilman, who had campaigned on a reform platform, was discovered to be every bit as _____ as the corrupt bosses he had railed against.
   a. clemency ... rampant
   b. discrepancy ... venial
   c. attainment ... altruistic
   d. irony ... venal

2. The senator found some _____ after her electoral defeat in the comforting knowledge that she would now be able to enjoy a life of _____, far from the strife of the political arena.
   a. esteem ... temerity
   b. solace ... repose
   c. panacea ... dearth
   d. clemency ... destitution

3. Nineteenth-century hucksters touted their elixirs as _____ for every ailment imaginable. Unfortunately, these concoctions often proved more _____ than the maladies they were supposed to cure.
   a. benefactors ... musty
   b. pinnacles ... ominous
   c. panaceas ... virulent
   d. attainments ... pungent

4. The school trustees agreed to cease their attempts to _____ the identity of the donor when an intermediary explained that the mysterious _____ wished to remain anonymous.
   a. comprise ... affiliation
   b. accede ... attainment
   c. ascertain ... benefactor
   d. esteem ... bequest

5. The salesman pressed me to sign the contract, but I refused to give my _____ to the agreement until all the terms and provisions he mentioned so vaguely were spelled out _____.
   a. discrepancy ... cogently
   b. esteem ... officiously
   c. temerity ... scrupulously
   d. assent ... explicitly

6. While it is true that human beings are neither _____ nor _____, they can certainly use what they do know to avoid making foolish or unnecessary mistakes.
   a. diffident ... supercilious
   b. omniscient ... infallible
   c. altruistic ... malevolent
   d. indomitable ... invulnerable

7. During the long years that the painter struggled to _____ fame, his talents never failed him. However, once he had actually achieved the public _____ that he sought, his skills began to desert him.
   a. attain ... esteem
   b. comprise ... nonchalance
   c. suppress ... clemency
   d. ascertain ... pinnacle

Idioms

In the essay "When the Wall Came Tumbling Down" (see pages 70–71), the author's grandmother is cited as saying that the Communist government built the Berlin Wall to "thumb its nose" at Western democracies.

"Thumb its nose" is an idiom, or idiomatic expression, that means "to show disrespect or scorn." **Idioms** are colorful expressions that mean something different from their literal meanings. There are thousands of idioms in the English language. Because idioms often "play" with language and are not literal, you can seldom figure out what they mean by analyzing the meaning of each word. For this reason, idioms often do not make sense when they are translated into another language, and they can be difficult to learn.

Choosing the Right Idiom

Read each sentence. Use context clues to figure out the meaning of each idiom in **boldface** *print. Then write the letter of the definition for the idiom in the sentence.*

1. Vickie, who always **keeps an ear to the ground**, knew about the corporate takeover long before it was announced. _____

2. Joe offered to **lend a hand** to the neighbors, who were moving some heavy furniture into storage. _____

3. If you want people here to trust you, you have to obey the rules and **keep your nose clean**. _____

4. If you would only **get off my back**, I could concentrate and get this finished more quickly. _____

5. If we **put our heads together**, maybe we can figure out this math problem. _____

6. The butler maintained his formal, detached manner, refusing to **let his hair down**. _____

7. The swindler was so convincing and seemed so honest that he really **pulled the wool over our eyes**. _____

8. I wanted to tell him that I thought he should dress up more for the party, but I **held my tongue**. _____

9. Don't **turn your back on** them now, when they need your help the most. _____

10. The best espresso machines from Italy cost **an arm and a leg**, so our café will have to survive without one. _____

a. work together to think through a problem

b. stay out of trouble

c. ignore; refuse to offer help

d. a large amount of money

e. relax; have fun

f. pays close attention to clues about what will happen

g. kept silent

h. stop pestering or annoying me

i. help someone complete a job

j. deceived us

Writing with Idioms

Find the meaning of each idiom. (Use an online or print dictionary if necessary.) Then write a sentence for each idiom.

1. all ears

_____

2. eye on the ball

_____

3. heart of gold

_____

4. head over heels

_____

5. a sweet tooth

_____

_____

6. pulling your leg

_____

_____

7. save your neck

_____

_____

8. caught red-handed

_____

9. in over your head

_____

10. tip of my tongue

_____

11. rub elbows with

_____

12. shake a leg

Denotation and Connotation

When you look up a word in a dictionary, you will find the word's **denotation**—its formal, literal meaning. A denotation is a straightforward, *neutral* definition of a word.

Many words have synonyms—words that share similar denotations. These synonyms often differ from one another in their shades of meaning, or **connotations**—the positive or negative emotional associations that people make to particular words.

Consider these synonyms for the neutral word *casual*.

> *relaxed*   *nonchalant*   *indifferent*   *apathetic*

Relaxed and *nonchalant* have positive connotations, suggesting ease, effortlessness, and a lack of formality. *Indifferent* and *apathetic*, however, suggest ease or casualness taken too far, to the point where there is carelessness and a lack of concern.

> **Think:** A golfer who has practiced for years may appear relaxed or nonchalant while playing, but a student who comes unprepared for a test appears indifferent and apathetic.

Look at these examples of words that are similar in denotation but have different connotations.

NEUTRAL	POSITIVE	NEGATIVE
agree	consent	acquiesce
strong	indomitable	implacable
thorough	scrupulous	fussy

To avoid miscommunication, be sure you understand a word's connotations before you use it in a particular context or situation. A word with a strongly positive or strongly negative connotation can change the entire tone of your message.

Shades of Meaning

Write a plus sign (+) in the box if the word has a positive connotation. Write a minus sign (–) if the word has a negative connotation. Put a zero (0) if the word is neutral.

1. altruistic ☐ **2.** inopportune ☐ **3.** attainments ☐ **4.** unfeigned ☐

5. malevolent ☐ **6.** virulent ☐ **7.** plodded ☐ **8.** chivalrous ☐

9. converge ☐ **10.** cogent ☐ **11.** ascertain ☐ **12.** supercilious ☐

13. diffident ☐ **14.** finite ☐ **15.** clemency ☐ **16.** officious ☐

WORD STUDY

Expressing the Connotation

Read each sentence. Select the word in parentheses that expresses the connotation (positive, negative, or neutral) given at the beginning of the sentence.

neutral **1.** We saw a young man (**skulking, roaming**) around the park this afternoon.

negative **2.** After she had time to think about it, she realized that her sister's (**casual, truculent**) criticism of her was born of jealousy.

positive **3.** You must be (**clever, omniscient**) if you can understand the motivations of all your team's players.

negative **4.** The situation seemed (**ominous, fateful**) to the queen, and she was convinced that nothing good could come of it.

neutral **5.** Some people like spicy foods, but the (**strong, pungent**) aroma of certain peppers and herbs does not appeal to me.

positive **6.** I think it was a(n) (**kind, altruistic**) impulse that prompted her to donate her annual bonus to the homeless shelter.

positive **7.** My grandfather loves to recite Shakespeare, and his performances of passages from the Bard's plays are (**infallible, skillful**).

neutral **8.** I greatly (**esteem, respect**) those who do good deeds anonymously, without any expectation of reward.

Challenge: Using Connotation

Choose vocabulary words from Units 4–6 to replace the highlighted words in the sentences below. Then explain how the connotation of the replacement word changes the tone of the sentence.

| temerity | panacea | embarked |
| bequeathed | stately | ironically |

1. Do you think he really believes that a four-hour workshop on getting along with others will be the **remedy** _____ that improves all of his relationships?

_____

_____

2. "You'll know that the train has arrived when you see it stop here," the attendant said wryly _____.

_____

_____

3. When the woman's will was read, everyone was surprised that she **left** _____ her entire estate to animal charities.

_____

_____

Classical Roots

fac, fact—to make or do

This root appears in **facile** (page 63). The literal meaning is "easily accomplished or done." Some other words based on the same root are listed below.

artifact	faction	factor	faculty
facility	factitious	factual	malefactor

From the list of words above, choose the one that corresponds to each of the brief definitions below. Write the word in the blank space in the illustrative sentence below the definition. Use an online or print dictionary if necessary.

1. ease, skill; that which serves or acts as a convenience or for a specific function

   By the time he was five years old, Mozart could play the piano with great _____.

2. a small group of people within a larger group

   The Senate _____ that opposed the president's budget was soundly defeated.

3. artificial, not natural; sham

   The enthusiasm of those cheering infomercial audiences seems to me to be _____.

4. an object of historical or archaeological interest produced by human workmanship (*"something made with skill"*)

   The museum has an outstanding collection of _____ from the pre-Columbian period.

5. one who commits a crime, evildoer (*"one who does evil"*)

   The _____ will stand trial for their terrible deeds.

6. one of the elements that help to bring about a result; an agent

   The ability to work together was a major _____ in the group's success.

7. a teaching staff; the ability to act or to do something

   A school may be known for its outstanding science _____.

8. based on fact; real

   Our assignment is to write a detailed _____ report on the presidential election.

*Read the following selection, taking note of the **boldface** words and their contexts. These words are among those you will be studying in Unit 7. As you complete the exercises in this unit, it may help to refer to the way the words are used below.*

Emmeline Pankhurst

＜Biographical Sketch＞

TIME magazine declared Emmeline Pankhurst to be "One of the 100 Most Important People of the 20th Century." Many people, though, have never heard of this influential woman and of how she transformed the lives of women in England at the beginning of that century.

Emmeline Goulden Pankhurst was born in 1858 to a wealthy family in Victorian England, where she proved a dutiful daughter, wife, and mother of five. She was also a **renegade**—an outspoken suffragist and a leader in the struggle to gain British women the right to vote. Mrs. Pankhurst (as she preferred to be called) was struck by an incongruous fact: Women could own property and pay taxes if they held a

Emmeline Pankhurst

job, but they had no legal right to vote. By 1903, the traditional women's suffrage organizations had met with little success. Disillusioned and angry over the government's backpedaling and broken promises, Pankhurst formed a more militant group, the Women's Social and Political Union (WSPU). The WSPU engaged in political activism: Members introduced **chaos** into a society that was used to order. They broke windows and started fires, shaking things up to draw attention to their cause. WSPU's battle cry was "Votes for Women!" Its motto was "Deeds, Not Words."

These were **turbulent** times. Most politicians (at this time, all men) were **vociferous** in their opposition to women's suffrage: They jeered and taunted and spoke as if they **abhorred** women. Newspapers published scathing, **corrosive** editorials that criticized the WSPU and its tactics. (One of London's daily papers originated the term *suffragette* to ridicule the protesters. The name stuck. In fact, WSPU members embraced it and used it themselves.)

Pankhurst (right) and fellow suffragettes were arrested in a 1910 protest and escorted to jail by police officers.

Some of the activities of the suffragettes—such as breaking windows and starting fires—were viewed as **reprehensible**, but the actions of the government, police, and prison wardens were worse. Women were battered and **buffeted** in demonstrations, and some were **implicated** in plots to destabilize straight-laced British society. Arrested protesters were jailed in **squalid** conditions, and many who **waived** their right to food to protest their incarceration were brutally force-fed. Pankhurst was imprisoned 12 times in one year alone in an attempt to **obviate** her continued participation in WSPU activities. During one court hearing, she said, "We are here, not because we are lawbreakers. We are here in our efforts to become law*makers*."

Pankurst influenced American suffragist Alice Paul, who led a celebrated march of 5,000 people—women and men—in Washington, D.C., in 1913. Paul had protested in London, been jailed, and forcibly fed, and this experience galvanized her into action when she returned home. The march she led was a turning point for U.S. women's suffrage, although it was to take seven more years before the 19th Amendment to the Constitution, giving women full voting rights, was ratified. Back in Britain, women over 30 were awarded the right to vote in 1918. Ten years later, the year Pankhurst died, the law was **amended**, and women were accorded the same voting rights as men.

Pankhurst's historical legacy is controversial. Some people view her as a forward- and clear-thinking heroine who had **discerned** the only effective way to get the vote for women. Critics say she was a self-serving **martinet** who demanded complete loyalty from her followers. One thing most can agree on: The determination and courage of one genteel, soft-spoken woman inspired a revolution, the effects of which persist to this day.

iWords

Snap the code, or go to **vocabularyworkshop.com**

Posters like this captured the imagination of women on both sides of the Atlantic.

Definitions

Note the spelling, pronunciation, part(s) of speech, and definition(s) of each of the following words. Then write the word in the blank spaces in the illustrative sentence(s) following. Finally, study the lists of synonyms and antonyms.

1. abhor
(ab hôr')

(*v.*) to regard with horror or loathing; to hate deeply

A pacifist is someone who _____ violence in all its forms.

SYNONYMS: detest, despise, abominate
ANTONYMS: admire, cherish, respect, relish

2. amend
(ə mend')

(*v.*) to change in a formal way; to change for the better

If you are not doing well in a particular subject, you may want to _____ your way of studying it.

SYNONYMS: modify, improve, correct

3. buffet
(bəf' ət)

(*v.*) to slap or cuff; to strike repeatedly; to drive or force with blows; to force one's way with difficulty; (*n.*) a slap, blow

Blinding snowstorms _____ the barren landmass of Antarctica for months on end.

Few figures in history or literature are as severely tested by fortune's _____ as Job in the Old Testament.

SYNONYMS: (*v.*) sock, thump, pummel, toss about

4. chaos
(kā' äs)

(*n.*) great confusion, disorder

A great many people lost their fortunes and even their lives in the _____ brought on by the French Revolution.

SYNONYMS: anarchy, turmoil
ANTONYMS: order, regularity, tranquillity

5. commodious
(kə mō' dē əs)

(*adj.*) roomy, spacious

No one would expect a tiny studio apartment to have particularly _____ closets.

SYNONYMS: comfortable, ample, capacious
ANTONYMS: cramped, claustrophobic, insufficient

6. corrosive
(kə rō' siv)

(*adj.*) eating away gradually, acidlike; bitterly sarcastic

Sulfuric acid is one of the most _____ substances known to chemistry.

SYNONYMS: caustic, mordant, acidulous, spiteful
ANTONYMS: bland, mild, benign, amiable

7. discern
(di sərn′)

(v.) to see clearly, recognize

It is a jury's job to _____ the truth by carefully evaluating all the evidence presented at trial.

SYNONYMS: perceive, detect, distinguish
ANTONYM: overlook

8. extant
(ek′ stənt)

(adj.) still existing; not exterminated, destroyed, or lost

The paintings of animals and human hands in Spain's Altamira caves are among the oldest _____ specimens of Stone Age art.

SYNONYMS: surviving, in existence
ANTONYMS: extinct, vanished

9. implicate
(im′ plə kāt)

(v.) to involve in; to connect with or be related to

The suspects never stood trial because there was no solid evidence to _____ them in the daring series of robberies.

SYNONYMS: incriminate, entangle
ANTONYMS: absolve, exculpate

10. inter
(in tər′)

(v.) to bury, commit to the earth; to consign to oblivion

Jewels and other objects once _____ with Egypt's pharaohs can now be seen in numerous museums all over the world.

ANTONYMS: unearth, exhume

11. martinet
(mär tə net′)

(n.) a strict disciplinarian; a stickler for the rules

When it came to drilling troops, the Revolutionary War general Baron Friedrich von Steuben was something of a

_____.

SYNONYMS: taskmaster, slave driver

12. obviate
(äb′ vē āt)

(v.) to anticipate and prevent; to remove, dispose of

Vaccinations can do much to _____ the dangers of childhood illnesses.

SYNONYMS: preclude, forestall, ward off

13. renegade
(ren′ ə gād)

(n.) one who leaves a group; a deserter, outlaw; (adj.) traitorous; unconventional, unorthodox

Many a writer has been labeled a _____ for refusing to conform to society's conventions.

_____ senators from the President's own party joined the opposition to defeat the bill.

SYNONYMS: (n.) turncoat, heretic
ANTONYMS: (n.) loyalist, patriot

14. reprehensible
(rep rē hen′ sə bəl)

(*adj.*) deserving blame or punishment

Stalin eliminated many potential rivals by accusing them of all sorts of _____ acts that they did not commit.

SYNONYMS: objectionable, blameworthy, culpable, odious
ANTONYMS: commendable, blameless, meritorious

15. somber
(säm′ bər)

(*adj.*) dark, gloomy; depressed or melancholy in spirit

The atmosphere in the locker room of the losing team could best be described as _____.

SYNONYMS: mournful, dismal
ANTONYMS: bright, sunny, lighthearted, jaunty

16. squalid
(skwäl′ id)

(*adj.*) filthy, wretched, debased

Many laws prohibit the types of _____ working conditions found in sweatshops.

SYNONYMS: dingy, sordid, foul, vile, abject
ANTONYMS: neat, spruce, exalted, lofty

17. turbulent
(tər′ byə lənt)

(*adj.*) disorderly, riotous, violent; stormy

Letters and diary entries may reveal a person's lifelong struggle to gain some control over _____ emotions.

SYNONYMS: tumultuous, unruly, agitated
ANTONYMS: calm, placid, tranquil, still

18. vociferous
(vō sif′ ə rəs)

(*adj.*) loud and noisy; compelling attention

Relief agencies regularly make _____ appeals for aid for victims of war, terrorism, and natural disasters.

SYNONYMS: clamorous, uproarious, blustering
ANTONYMS: quiet, soft-spoken, muted, subdued

19. voluminous
(və lü′ mə nəs)

(*adj.*) of great size; numerous; writing or speaking at great length

The task of summarizing the _____ reports issued by government agencies may fall to members of a legislator's staff.

SYNONYMS: bulky, massive, plentiful
ANTONYMS: scant, meager

20. waive
(wāv)

(*v.*) to do without, give up voluntarily; to put off temporarily, defer

The senator agreed to _____ opposition to the proposed bill if some of its more controversial provisions were substantially modified.

SYNONYMS: decline, relinquish, forgo
ANTONYMS: claim, accept

Choosing the Right Word

*Select the **boldface** word that better completes each sentence. You might refer to the selection on pages 88–89 to see how most of these words are used in context.*

1. In 1940, Winston Churchill conveyed to the British people the (**somber, voluminous**) truth that they were fighting for their national existence.

2. When he accused me of playing fast and loose with the rules, I lost my temper and called him an officious (**renegade, martinet**).

3. Hoping it was not too late to (**amend, waive**) their relationship, the young man purchased a lovely bouquet of roses.

4. I'm not so sure that I want to rent a bungalow so (**squalid, commodious**) that I'll have room for guests every weekend.

5. We can expect (**chaos, martinets**) later if we do not develop a realistic conservation policy now.

Winston Churchill, prime minister of England during World War II, was dedicated to the defeat of Hitler and the Nazis.

6. Instead of trying to help the people who had elected him, he became involved in a (**squalid, extant**) little quarrel about handing out jobs.

7. We sometimes forget that the great men who led our revolution were considered (**renegades, buffets**) by the British king.

8. The Tech team was offside on the play; but since we had thrown them for an eight-yard loss, we (**waived, abhorred**) the five-yard penalty.

9. Didn't it occur to them that by signing the letter "Sophomores of Central High," they would (**implicate, waive**) the entire class in the protest?

10. I wouldn't say that I (**inter, abhor**) housework, but I must admit that I avoid it whenever I can.

11. Some people prefer the (**discernment, turbulence**) of life in a big city to the more placid atmosphere of a small town.

12. At lunchtime, the room rang with the sound of (**reprehensible, vociferous**) debates between the fans of rival teams.

13. The custom by which a young man buys his bride through a payment to her father is still (**commodious, extant**) in some parts of the world.

14. Did you know that many soft drinks, especially colas, are so (**corrosive, reprehensible**) that they can erode tooth enamel over time?

15. The Founding Fathers set up a method of (**amending, obviating**) the Constitution that is neither too easy nor too difficult to use.

16. A lack of organizational skills can make a student's life (**commodious, chaotic**) right before a busy exam season.

17. According to cryptozoologists—people who search for proof that legendary creatures exist—Bigfoot might be a large prehistoric humanoid that is still (**vociferous, extant**).

18. Which great poet said that his head was "bloody but unbowed" under the (**buffeting, chaos**) of fate?

19. I don't know which was more (**reprehensible, somber**)—making improper use of the money or lying about it later.

20. History gives us many examples of how the (**vociferous, corrosive**) effects of religious hatred can weaken the entire social structure.

21. Even in his old age, Thomas Jefferson kept up a (**voluminous, turbulent**) correspondence with important people in America and abroad.

22. The time has come for us to (**implicate, inter**) our ancient disputes and go forward as a truly united people.

23. A compromise agreement reached in the judge's chambers would clearly (**discern, obviate**) the need for a long, costly lawsuit.

24. If you examine the evidence carefully, you will soon (**discern, amend**) the contradictions in the witness's story.

25. If you (**obviate, abhor**) blood, then you should probably not be a nurse.

Synonyms

*Choose the word from this unit that is the same or most nearly the same in meaning as the **boldface** word or expression in the phrase. Write that word on the line. Use a dictionary if necessary.*

1. battered by fluctuations in the stock market _____

2. a **vast** and elegant hotel lobby _____

3. noticed a change in public opinion _____

4. a treasure **laid to rest** _____

5. willing to **alter** long-standing company policy _____

6. avert further debate _____

7. the **solemn** tolling of church bells _____

8. condemned by all as a **defector** _____

9. a formerly endangered, now **thriving** species _____

10. copious pieces of evidence _____

Antonyms

*Choose the word from this unit that is most nearly opposite in meaning to the **boldface** word or expression in the phrase. Write that word on the line. Use a dictionary if necessary.*

1. seeking **confined** lodging _____

2. **dug up** the ancient king's remains _____

3. took **succinct** notes during the meeting _____

4. a custom thought to be **defunct** _____

5. the **cheerful** face of the lottery winner _____

Completing the Sentence

From the words in this unit, choose the one that best completes each of the following sentences. Write the word in the space provided.

1. It is particularly _____ for citizens to fail to vote in national elections and then complain about the government.

2. The records of the school board meeting on the proposed bond issue are so _____ that it would take me a week to read them.

3. A person who changes from one political party to another on the basis of honest conviction should not be regarded as a(n) _____.

4. I didn't expect you to like my suggestion, but I was shocked by your bitter and _____ criticism of it.

5. One of the signs of maturity is the ability to _____ the difference between things that are secondary and things that are truly important.

6. Although our drill instructor was determined to follow the rules, he was by no means an overbearing _____.

7. The trunk of the car was so _____ that it held all of our skiing equipment as well as our other luggage.

8. We Americans are proud that each change of the national administration, far from being _____, is carried out in a peaceful and friendly manner.

9. Who would not feel depressed on entering that _____ old courtroom, with its dim lighting and dark, massive furnishings?

10. Confident that she could present the case effectively to a judge, the lawyer advised her client to _____ his right to a jury trial.

11. The American writer Dorothy Parker was celebrated for her sharp tongue and _____ wit.

12. In a natural history museum, we can see physical remains of many species of animals that are no longer _____ .

13. Getting a good education will do much to _____ the problem of finding a job that pays well.

14. Shakespeare tells us that "the evil that men do lives after them; the good is oft _____ with their bones."

15. Those accused of crimes are sometimes willing to _____ their accomplices in return for immunity from prosecution.

16. Let me say frankly that I _____ prejudice in anyone, even a member of my own family.

17. Are we justified in showing visitors only the most attractive and interesting sections of our cities, towns, or villages while keeping them away from the _____ neighborhoods where so many people live?

18. In our frantic search for the missing papers, we overturned everything in the room, leaving it in complete _____.

19. We are petitioning the council to _____ its procedures so that all citizens will have a chance to express their opinions.

20. A person who has been _____ about by many dreadful misfortunes will either become stronger or suffer a complete breakdown.

Writing: Words in Action

1. Look back at "Emmeline Pankhurst" (pages 88–89). Suppose that you are a citizen living during Pankhurst's time. Write an editorial in which you express your views about women's suffrage. Support your view using at least two details from the passage and three unit words.

2. *"The moment we begin to fear the opinions of others and hesitate to tell the truth that is in us, and from motives of policy are silent when we should speak, the divine floods of light and life no longer flow into our souls."*—Elizabeth Cady Stanton

   Do you agree with Stanton's observation about the need to speak up about certain issues instead of remaining silent? Write a brief essay in which you support your opinion of Stanton's statement, using examples from the reading (pages 88–89) as well as your own knowledge and experience. Write at least three paragraphs, and use three or more words from this unit.

Vocabulary in Context

Literary Text

The following excerpts are from the novel Oliver Twist *by Charles Dickens. Some of the words you have studied in this unit appear in* **boldface** *type. Complete each statement below the excerpt by circling the letter of the correct answer.*

1. But now that he was enveloped in the old calico robes which had grown yellow in the same service, he was badged and ticketed, and fell into his place at once—a parish child—the orphan of a workhouse—the humble, half-starved drudge—to be cuffed and **buffeted** through the world—despised by all, and pitied by none.

   A **buffeted** person will be

   a. served food **c.** sheltered and protected
   b. knocked around **d.** pampered and praised

2. At this moment the noise grew louder. Sikes, again looking round, could **discern** that the men who had given chase were already climbing the gate of the field in which he stood; and that a couple of dogs were some paces in advance of them.

   To **discern** activity is to

   a. value it **c.** observe it
   b. stop it **d.** critique it

3. "When is it to be done?" asked Nancy, stopping some **turbulent** exclamation on the part of Mr. Sikes, expressive of the disgust with which he received Fagin's affectation of humanity.

   A **turbulent** exclamation is most likely

   a. fierce **c.** soothing
   b. irrelevant **d.** ironic

Oliver making his famous plea, "Please, sir, I want some more," in the 1948 film.

4. The stars seemed, to the boy's eyes, farther from the earth than he had ever seen them before; there was no wind; and the **somber** shadows thrown by the trees upon the ground, looked sepulchral and death-like, from being so still.

   Somber shadows are

   a. distinctive **c.** sprightly
   b. elongated **d.** ominous

5. The houses on either side were high and large, but very old, and tenanted by people of the poorest class: as their neglected appearance would have sufficiently denoted, without the concurrent testimony afforded by the **squalid** looks of the few men and women who, with folded arms and bodies half doubled, occasionally skulked along.

   A **squalid** appearance is NOT

   a. neglected **c.** grimy
   b. respectable **d.** miserable

Interactive Quiz

Snap the code, or go to **vocabularyworkshop.com**

Read the following selection, taking note of the **boldface** words and their contexts. These words are among those you will be studying in Unit 8. As you complete the exercises in this unit, it may help to refer to the way the words are used below.

Anita Stockton Talks about Risk and Reward on the Stock Market

<Interview with an Expert>

By Jon X. Paek
Published April 19, 2012

Although *the stock market affects all Americans—both those who invest in the market and those who don't—many people have little or no understanding of how it works. This reporter sat down with Anita Stockton, a retired stockbroker, to find out more about this important financial institution.*

JXP: What does the stock market do?
AS: The stock market plays a crucial role in the global economy, enabling companies to raise money by selling shares of ownership to investors. The cash generated by sales of stock helps many companies grow, which increases competition and growth in the economy and provides consumers with more goods and services at cheaper prices.

JXP: Some people get rich from the stock market. How do they make money?
AS: Owners of shares, or shareholders, seek to profit from investments in stocks, but there are no guarantees. Occasionally, some companies distribute dividends, a sum of money to shareholders for each share they own. Shareholders also sell their shares to other investors through a stock exchange, and they may **revel** in their profits when they sell for more than the original cost. Stock trading has become increasingly complex, with thousands of companies publicly traded and **multifarious** strategies available to traders. But "buy low, sell high" is a rule that will never become **obsolete** and that investors will always **commend**.

JXP: Sounds like easy money. Is there risk involved?
AS: Unfortunately, there is no sure way to predict fluctuations in stock prices. There can be **reprisals** for careless investing. The market can be an **omnivorous** beast that will pick clean the portfolios of the savviest investors. Even the wise lose more money than they gain, so putting one's money in the stock market is not for the **ingenuous**. Stock analysts measure the value of a company in terms of its assets, debts, and earnings. But such analysts cannot project future earnings with certainty. Nevertheless, when analysts determine that a company is likely to grow faster than its competitors, investors rush to purchase shares. Consequently, demand for the company's stock increases along with expectations for future performance, and the price of the shares rises. When the company's earnings are **compatible** with expectations, the share price may continue to rise. Investors keep their shares in anticipation of further gains or sell for a profit at the

payoffs, like government bonds. Conversely, many a daring investor in the stock market has **derided** himself for his insatiable appetite for risk once he felt the sting of losses. The volatility of the market scares many investors away and punishes the imprudent.

JXP: With so much uncertainty, who invests in the stock market?
AS: For many investors, the possible gains of the stock market prove too great to ignore. Disciplined investors balance potential losses against potential rewards. They diversify their investments, maintaining reasonable expectations and a moderate appetite for risk. They research the companies whose stocks they buy. In short, **apathy** is not recommended for potential investors, but if you have no interest in studying the market yourself, mutual funds and money managers can fill this role, affording you the opportunity to benefit from the power of the stock market and from professional expertise. Overall, cautious, prudent, and well-informed investment in the stock market has proven to be one of the best ways for investors to increase their wealth.

new price. Sometimes, a company's profits may fall short of expectations, and such results, once reported, can have a **stultifying** effect on the demand for the firm's stock. **Apprehensive** investors watch the value of their investment shrink as the share price drops.

JXP: What a roller-coaster ride! Do many people lose money?
AS: The uncertainties of the stock market put many would-be investors in a **quandary**. Some investors regard the stock market with **animosity** and buy low-risk investments with **parsimonious**

Snap the code, or go to **vocabularyworkshop.com**

Wall Street on the Black Monday stock market crash of October 18, 1987

Definitions

Note the spelling, pronunciation, part(s) of speech, and definition(s) of each of the following words. Then write the word in the blank spaces in the illustrative sentence(s) following. Finally, study the lists of synonyms and antonyms.

1. animosity
(an ə mäs′ ə tē)

(*n.*) strong dislike; bitter hostility

The deep _____ between the Montagues and Capulets could not prevent Romeo and Juliet from falling in love.

SYNONYMS: enmity, rancor, antipathy
ANTONYMS: affection, fondness, rapport, amity

2. apathy
(ap′ ə thē)

(*n.*) a lack of feeling, emotion, or interest

I was horrified when the sales force greeted my great idea for an ad campaign with total _____.

SYNONYMS: indifference, disinterest, detachment
ANTONYMS: enthusiasm, fervor, ardor, concern

3. apprehensive
(ap rē hen′ siv)

(*adj.*) fearful or anxious, especially about the future

As the hurricane approached, _____ residents all along the coast prepared for the worst.

SYNONYMS: worried, nervous, fretful, jittery
ANTONYMS: unworried, assured, confident, certain

4. commend
(kə mend′)

(*v.*) to praise, express approval; to present as worthy of attention; to commit to the care of

The mayor _____ the young people for their volunteer work at local hospitals and soup kitchens.

SYNONYMS: applaud, entrust
ANTONYMS: abhor, loathe

5. compatible
(kəm pat′ ə bəl)

(*adj.*) able to get along or work well together; capable of use with some other model or system

Eyewitness accounts of an accident rarely are totally

_____.

SYNONYMS: harmonious, in agreement
ANTONYMS: mismatched, incongruous, antagonistic

6. condolence
(kən dō′ ləns)

(*n.*) an expression of sympathy

A few well-chosen words of _____ can be a great comfort to someone who has lost a loved one.

SYNONYMS: commiseration, solace, sympathy

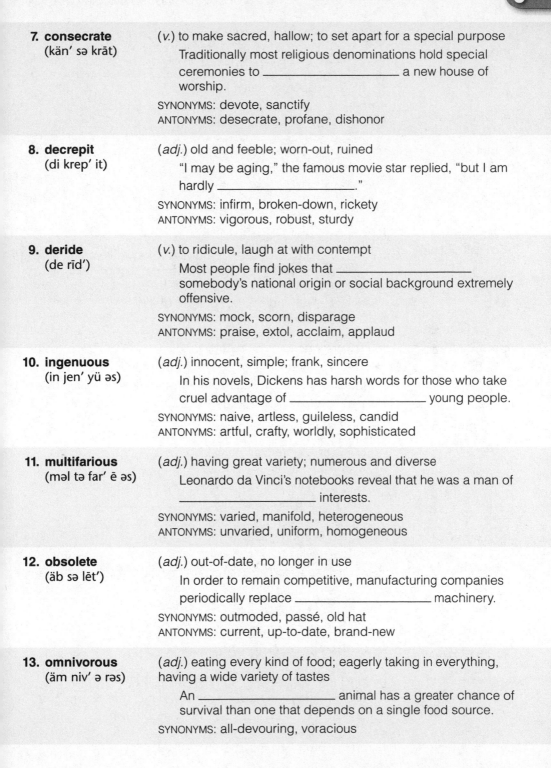

7. consecrate
(kän′ sə krāt)

(*v.*) to make sacred, hallow; to set apart for a special purpose

Traditionally most religious denominations hold special ceremonies to _____ a new house of worship.

SYNONYMS: devote, sanctify
ANTONYMS: desecrate, profane, dishonor

8. decrepit
(di krep′ it)

(*adj.*) old and feeble; worn-out, ruined

"I may be aging," the famous movie star replied, "but I am hardly _____."

SYNONYMS: infirm, broken-down, rickety
ANTONYMS: vigorous, robust, sturdy

9. deride
(de rīd′)

(*v.*) to ridicule, laugh at with contempt

Most people find jokes that _____ somebody's national origin or social background extremely offensive.

SYNONYMS: mock, scorn, disparage
ANTONYMS: praise, extol, acclaim, applaud

10. ingenuous
(in jen′ yü əs)

(*adj.*) innocent, simple; frank, sincere

In his novels, Dickens has harsh words for those who take cruel advantage of _____ young people.

SYNONYMS: naive, artless, guileless, candid
ANTONYMS: artful, crafty, worldly, sophisticated

11. multifarious
(məl tə far′ ē əs)

(*adj.*) having great variety; numerous and diverse

Leonardo da Vinci's notebooks reveal that he was a man of _____ interests.

SYNONYMS: varied, manifold, heterogeneous
ANTONYMS: unvaried, uniform, homogeneous

12. obsolete
(äb sə lēt′)

(*adj.*) out-of-date, no longer in use

In order to remain competitive, manufacturing companies periodically replace _____ machinery.

SYNONYMS: outmoded, passé, old hat
ANTONYMS: current, up-to-date, brand-new

13. omnivorous
(äm niv′ ə rəs)

(*adj.*) eating every kind of food; eagerly taking in everything, having a wide variety of tastes

An _____ animal has a greater chance of survival than one that depends on a single food source.

SYNONYMS: all-devouring, voracious

14. parsimonious
(pär sə mō' nē əs)

(*adj.*) stingy, miserly; meager, poor, small

Many people who lost money in the Great Depression later adhered to a _____ lifestyle, even during more prosperous times.

SYNONYMS: frugal, niggardly, penny-pinching, cheap
ANTONYMS: generous, openhanded

15. quandary
(kwän' drē)

(*n.*) a state of perplexity or doubt

Try as I might, I could see no way out of the ethical _____ in which I found myself.

SYNONYMS: confusion, dilemma, predicament

16. recalcitrant
(ri kal' sə trənt)

(*adj.*) stubbornly disobedient, resisting authority

A _____ individual may have great difficulty adjusting to a job that requires a good deal of teamwork.

SYNONYMS: unruly, obstinate, contrary, ornery
ANTONYMS: obedient, docile, compliant

17. reprisal
(ri prī' zəl)

(*n.*) an injury done in return for injury

The Highland clans of Scotland engaged in cattle rustling in _____ for real or imagined injuries.

SYNONYMS: retaliation, revenge

18. revel
(rev' əl)

(*v.*) to take great pleasure in; (*n.*) a wild celebration

Some movie stars do not _____ in the attention that their fans and the media pay them.

All around the world, the new millennium was ushered in with positive thoughts and _____ .

SYNONYMS: (*v.*) relish, savor, bask in, carouse
ANTONYMS: (*v.*) abhor, loathe

19. stultify
(stəl' tə fī)

(*v.*) to make ineffective or useless, cripple; to have a dulling effect on

Oppressive heat may _____ the mind and spirit as well as the body.

SYNONYMS: smother, stifle, neutralize, negate
ANTONYMS: arouse, excite, inspire, stimulate

20. suave
(swäv)

(*adj.*) smoothly agreeable or polite; pleasing to the senses

Nick Charles, the clever detective in the *Thin Man* movies, is a _____ man-about-town.

SYNONYMS: sophisticated, urbane, polished
ANTONYMS: crude, clumsy, oafish, loutish

Mary Shelley wrote
Frankenstein, popular
even during its first
publication in 1818.

Choosing the Right Word

*Select the **boldface** word that better completes each sentence. You might refer to the essay on pages 98–99 to see how most of these words are used in context.*

1. Mary Shelley is often (**commended, stultified**) for having written one of the earliest examples of science fiction: the classic novel *Frankenstein.*

2. The woman looked (**parsimonious, apprehensive**) when her guide announced that the group was going whitewater rafting in the afternoon.

3. In this new century of our nation's life, let us (**stultify, consecrate**) ourselves anew to the ideals of human freedom.

4. Your unwillingness to study foreign languages is in no way (**compatible, omnivorous**) with your ambition to get a job in the foreign service.

5. Although our society must punish criminals, I don't think we should do so simply as a (**reprisal, quandary**) for the wrongs they have committed.

6. Many stand-up comedians regularly (**revel, deride**) popular fads and fashions.

7. I must give you the sad news that correct spelling and good grammar are not, and never will be, (**obsolete, decrepit**).

8. Can you be so (**apprehensive, ingenuous**) that you don't realize she is paying us all those phony compliments to get something out of us?

9. The handful of (**compatible, recalcitrant**) students who refuse to obey study hall regulations are violating the rights of the majority.

10. The address was so dull and long-winded that it seemed to (**consecrate, stultify**) rather than inspire the audience.

11. Yes, there is some (**apathy, animosity**) between different racial and ethnic groups, but it can be overcome by education and experience.

12. The owner of the used car dealership showed poor judgment when he decided to publicly (**deride, revel**) his employees' suggestions for improved customer service.

13. Two of the chief strengths of modern American society are the variety and vitality that arise from its (**multifarious, obsolete**) cultures.

14. Clark Gable was a(n) (**obsolete, suave**) leading man who attracted women with his charm and good looks and impressed men with his strength and confidence.

15. Her moods seem to go from one extreme to the other—from deepest (**apathy, animosity**) to unlimited enthusiasm.

16. He is so absorbed in himself that he has become (**parsimonious, suave**) in the normal expression of human sympathy and affection.

17. So we are faced with that old (**quandary, reprisal**)—an income that simply can't be stretched to cover the things that we simply must have.

18. The headwaiter was so (**suave, ingenuous**) and self-assured in his manner that we took him for a diplomat.

19. If you can't (**deride, commend**) me for my efforts to help you, at least don't criticize me for not doing everything you want.

20. Those students who have been doing their work all term need not feel (**apprehensive, recalcitrant**) about the final examination.

21. When my friends appeared with an MP3 player and a docking station with amazing sound, I realized that our crash study session might become an all-day (**reprisal, revel**).

22. I think we should offer congratulations rather than (**revels, condolences**) for the disappearance of that battered old heap you called a car.

23. Some people are (**omnivorous, parsimonious**) readers, with a lively appetite for all types of fiction and nonfiction.

24. Our Constitution is more than 200 years old; but far from being (**suave, decrepit**), it is still a vital, dynamic, and highly practical plan of government.

25. I am looking for a printer that is (**compatible, ingenuous**) with my computer.

Synonyms

*Choose the word from this unit that is the same or most nearly the same in meaning as the **boldface** word or expression in the phrase. Write that word on the line. Use a dictionary if necessary.*

1. dedicated themselves to healing the sick _____

2. cruel acts of **retribution** _____

3. delegated to the care of friends _____

4. sent a sincere message of **empathy** _____

5. courting the most **debonair** bachelor _____

6. jeered at by the protesters _____

7. surrounded by **like-minded** friends _____

8. babysitting a **cantankerous** child _____

9. rejected the author's **antiquated** theories _____

10. an old house with a **dilapidated** porch _____

Antonyms

*Choose the word from this unit that is most nearly opposite in meaning to the **boldface** word or expression in the phrase. Write that word on the line. Use a dictionary if necessary.*

1. a person with **unpolished** manners _____

2. to **defile** a national memorial _____

3. an **energetic** contender _____

4. a thoroughly **cooperative** individual _____

5. **callousness** in response to your loss _____

Completing the Sentence

From the words in this unit, choose the one that best completes each of the following sentences. Write the word in the space provided.

1. "Today," said the speaker, "we _____ this monument to the memory of all those who fought and died in defense of their country."

2. If you think of all the different kinds of food that human beings are able to consume, you will realize that we are truly a(n) _____ species.

3. From all his growling and snapping, you would think our beagle felt a personal _____ toward every other dog on the block.

4. So there I was, having accepted invitations to two different parties on the same evening. What a(n) _____ to be in!

5. It is surprising how often people with very different personalities turn out to be _____ when they get to know one another.

6. Although I was unable to visit my old friend's widow in person, I offered my _____ in a heartfelt letter.

7. Political candidates who do nothing but _____ their opponents' character and abilities may alienate voters.

8. In totalitarian regimes, censorship and violence are often employed to suppress criticism and _____ dissent.

9. The _____ problems that will face America's presidents in the twenty-first century will make their job one of the most demanding in the world.

10. Technology changes so rapidly that a particular computer may be state-of-the-art one day and _____ the next.

11. Throughout the hot, dusty journey, we _____ in the thought that soon we would be swimming in the cool lake.

12. I think that the phrase "on its last legs" is an apt description of that _____ old house down the block.

13. It was difficult for us to believe that such a _____ and cultured gentleman was a member of a gang of international jewel thieves.

14. Simple _____ seems to be the main reason that such a large percentage of those eligible to vote fail to cast ballots in any election.

15. Struggling to overcome her _____ inclinations, she finally reached into her pocket and handed me one thin dime!

16. I trust you will never have the experience of trying to cross the desert with a(n) _____ mule that wants to remain where it is.

17. The board of directors voted to _____ him for the skill and enthusiasm with which he had managed the charity drive.

18. In spite of all the elaborate safety precautions, I couldn't help feeling a little _____ as I set out for my first skydiving lesson.

19. If we increase our tariff rates on the goods of other countries, we can be sure that they will raise their own rates in _____.

20. Now that I am a senior, it is hard to believe that I was ever as innocent and _____ as the members of the new freshman class.

Writing: Words in Action

1. Look back at the interview with Anita Stockton (pages 98–99). Write your own financial advice column for teens in which you explain the pros and cons of investing in the stock market. Use at least two details from the passage and three unit words.

2. *"An investment in knowledge pays the best interest."* —Benjamin Franklin

Do you agree with Franklin's statement? In what ways can you "invest" in knowledge, and how can you gain "interest" from that investment? Write a brief essay in which you explain what Franklin means and demonstrate how his observation applies to your own life. Use examples from the reading (pages 98–99) as well as from your own observations and personal knowledge. Write at least three paragraphs, and use three or more words from this unit.

Vocabulary in Context

Literary Text

The following excerpts are from **The Three Musketeers** *by Alexandre Dumas. Some of the words you have studied in this unit appear in* **boldface** *type. Complete each statement below the excerpt by circling the letter of the correct answer.*

1. "On guard, then!" cried Athos.

Immediately eight swords glittered in the rays of the setting sun, and the combat began with an **animosity** very natural between men twice enemies.

A fight provoked by **animosity** is rooted in

a. kindness   **c.** hostility
b. familiarity   **d.** respect

2. "As to the other, he knows me, he fears me, and knows what he has to expect of me if ever I escape from his hands. It is useless, then, to attempt anything with him. But Felton—that's another thing. He is a young, **ingenuous**, pure man who seems virtuous; him there are means of destroying."

Someone who is **ingenuous** is NOT

a. devious   **c.** honorable
b. naive   **d.** trusting

3. The result of these reflections was that d'Artagnan, without asking information of any kind, alighted, **commended** the horses to the care of his lackey, [and] entered a small room destined to receive those who wished to be alone....

When something is **commended** to the care of another, it is

a. recommended   **c.** sent into exile
b. handed over   **d.** fussed over

Frank Finlay, Oliver Reed, Michael York, and Richard Chamberlain portray the talented swordsmen in the 1973 film *The Three Musketeers*.

4. "...[I]t is fit you should know, Monsieur d'Artagnan, that I have received heavy and serious complaints against you. You do not **consecrate** your days and nights wholly to the king's service."

To **consecrate** means to

a. acclaim   **c.** violate
b. adjust   **d.** dedicate

5. "There only remains, then, the question of the five shillings to be settled. You think me rather **parsimonious**, don't you? That's because I don't care to leave you the means of corrupting your jailers."

Someone who is **parsimonious** is

a. wicked   **c.** thrifty
b. wasteful   **d.** arrogant

Interactive Quiz

Snap the code, or go to
vocabularyworkshop.com

*Read the following selection, taking note of the **boldface** words and their contexts. These words are among those you will be studying in Unit 9. As you complete the exercises in this unit, it may help to refer to the way the words are used below.*

My Last Day in Pompeii
<Diary Entry>

August 26, 79

I arrived in Pompeii the day before the volcano Vesuvius swallowed the city. Our ships were heavy with Syrian goods: leather works, dyes, and silk. I oversaw the men unloading the cargo, and when this job was done, I set out with two companions into the city. After our long journey, I **exulted** at the prospect of a decent meal and assumed my friends' desire to satisfy their appetites was as **ardent** as my own. One of them surprised me with a **spontaneous** plan: He insisted that we **deviate** from our goal to stop at the Temple of Fortuna Augusta.

If only we'd had an **inkling** of the city's fate, how many lives would have been spared! But who can predict the whims of the **capricious** gods? Having made our

offering in haste, we descended the steps of the temple in a rush to fill our stomachs. We passed the market, winding through crowds of people carrying foodstuffs they had purchased: meat and fish, fruits, breads and cakes. Soon we found a restaurant and sat down to the business of eating grilled goat meat, **copious** servings of vegetables cooked in fish sauce, and a **palatable** wine. Satisfied, we made our way to the baths to wash off the grime of our voyage.

I parted ways with my companions and walked to the home of Marcus Durmius, a wealthy merchant who

Amphorae were used to transport goods on ships.

People fled Pompeii as the volcano Vesuvius covered the town in ash.

had invited me to be his guest. Along the way, I noticed an **emaciated** old nobleman dressed in purple silk. As our paths crossed, the ground trembled—one of those minor quakes with which the inhabitants of Pompeii were all too familiar. Afraid the nobleman might fall, I grabbed him by the arm to steady him. The tremor passed, but rather than thank me for my trouble, the old man looked at me with **rancor**, as if I had been impudent to assist him, and he walked off without a word.

I spent the rest of the day with Marcus Durmius in his garden. We exchanged news and discussed the price of wine, staring at the **limpid** water of his fountain, which was surrounded by the **gnarled** branches of his laurel trees. Excited by my report of prices in the East, the **assiduous** merchant outlined a plan for us to ship his wine immediately for sale in Palmyra. I awoke early in the morning and returned to the harbor to make the arrangements, and it was there, awaiting Marcus Durmius's porters, that I felt the shock of Vesuvius's eruption.

Looking over the city, I saw a plume of smoke climbing into the air. An uproar swept over the harbor, the shouts of men overwhelming the sounds of the bay. We watched in horror as the cloud approached, showering the temples in dust, setting rooftops ablaze. Our captain,

recognizing the sign of an **omnipotent** god determined to **chastise** the city's inhabitants, commanded that we fill our vessel with as many souls as it could carry, and within two hours we were at sea. In the distance we now saw a second column of smoke rise from the mountain, much larger than the first, like a sinister tree sprouting in the sky. We watched the **poignant** scene as this new cloud spread over the city, and we were certain that Pompeii was doomed.

iWords

Snap the code, or go to
vocabularyworkshop.com

The city of Pompeii
as it looks today

Definitions

Note the spelling, pronunciation, part(s) of speech, and definition(s) of each of the following words. Then write the word in the blank spaces in the illustrative sentence(s) following. Finally, study the lists of synonyms and antonyms.

1. allocate
(al′ ə kāt)

(*v.*) to set apart or designate for a special purpose; to distribute

In their wills many people _____ a portion of their wealth to favorite charities or educational institutions.

SYNONYMS: assign, allot, distribute

2. ardent
(är′ dənt)

(*adj.*) very enthusiastic, impassioned

The members of the winning team acknowledged the cheers of their _____ fans.

SYNONYMS: intense, fervent, avid
ANTONYMS: indifferent, stolid, phlegmatic, apathetic

3. assiduous
(ə sij′ ü əs)

(*adj.*) persistent, attentive, diligent

Workers who are conscientious in the performance of their duties are, by definition, _____.

SYNONYMS: industrious, unremitting, sedulous
ANTONYMS: lazy, lackadaisical, shiftless

4. brash
(brash)

(*adj.*) prone to act in a hasty manner; impudent

Successful political candidates soon learn how to handle tough questions fired at them by _____ newspaper and TV reporters.

SYNONYMS: rash, impetuous, brazen
ANTONYMS: prudent, wary, circumspect

5. capricious
(kə prish′ əs)

(*adj.*) subject to whims or passing fancies

Our constitutional system of checks and balances is designed to prevent the _____ use of power by any branch of the federal government.

SYNONYMS: impulsive, fickle, unpredictable, mercurial
ANTONYMS: constant, steady, unwavering

6. chastise
(chas tīz′)

(*v.*) to inflict physical punishment as a means of correction; to scold severely

State and federal laws now forbid the use of corporal punishment to _____ prisoners.

SYNONYMS: discipline, censure
ANTONYMS: commend, reward

7. copious
(kō′ pē əs)

(*adj.*) abundant; plentiful; wordy, verbose

The _____ and detailed footnotes found in most scholarly books are designed to document the authors' sources.

SYNONYMS: ample, profuse, bountiful
ANTONYMS: inadequate, meager, scanty, concise

8. deviate
(*v.*, dē′ vē āt; *n.*, *adj.*, dē′ vē ət)

(*v.*) to turn aside; to stray from a norm; (*n.*) one who departs from a norm; (*adj.*) differing from a norm, heterodox, unconventional

Try not to _____ from the directions given in the owner's manual.

Those who disagreed with the Soviet form of government were often branded as _____ and imprisoned.

Under our system of justice, the mentally ill cannot be held responsible for their _____ behavior.

SYNONYMS: (*v.*) diverge, veer, swerve
ANTONYMS: (*v.*) conform to, abide by; (*adj.*) orthodox

9. emaciated
(i mā′ shē ā tid)

(*adj.*, *part.*) unnaturally thin

People who suffer from serious eating disorders may soon become woefully _____.

SYNONYMS: withered, shriveled
ANTONYMS: plump, fat, obese, corpulent

10. exult
(eg zəlt′)

(*v.*) to rejoice greatly

The campaign workers _____ in the unexpected victory of their candidate.

SYNONYMS: revel, glory
ANTONYMS: mope, sulk, regret, rue, lament

11. gnarled
(närld)

(*adj.*) knotted, twisted, lumpy

The _____ limbs of cypresses dominate many of the landscapes painted by the Dutch artist Vincent van Gogh.

SYNONYMS: knotty, misshapen, contorted
ANTONYMS: smooth, unblemished, straight

12. indemnity
(in dem′ nə tē)

(*n.*) a payment for damage or loss

A certain type of life insurance contract provides double _____ for the accidental death of the policyholder.

SYNONYMS: compensation, reparation

13. inkling
(iŋk' liŋ)

(*n.*) a hint; a vague notion
I had absolutely no _____ of what to expect as I entered the room.
SYNONYMS: clue, intimation, suggestion

14. limpid
(lim' pid)

(*adj.*) clear, transparent; readily understood
Snorkelers flock to the _____ waters of the Caribbean to view schools of brightly colored fish.
SYNONYMS: lucid, intelligible; ANTONYMS: murky, opaque

15. omnipotent
(äm nip' ə tənt)

(*adj.*) almighty, having unlimited power or authority
Many of the heroes of ancient myths and legends appear to be all but _____.
SYNONYM: all-powerful; ANTONYMS: powerless, impotent, weak

16. palatable
(pal' ə tə bəl)

(*adj.*) agreeable to the taste or one's sensibilities; suitable for consumption
The addition of some seasonings will usually make even the blandest of dishes _____.
SYNONYMS: edible, appetizing, attractive
ANTONYMS: inedible, distasteful, disagreeable

17. poignant
(poin' yənt)

(*adj.*) deeply affecting, touching; keen or sharp in taste or smell
There is something truly _____ about the sight of falling leaves in autumn.
SYNONYMS: heartrending, melancholy
ANTONYMS: unaffecting, bland, vapid, insipid, funny

18. rancor
(raŋ' kər)

(*n.*) bitter resentment or ill-will
An unusual degree of _____ may creep into the tone of the political debate in an election year.
SYNONYMS: animosity, enmity, bitterness
ANTONYMS: goodwill, harmony, rapport, amity

19. sophomoric
(säf ə môr' ik)

(*adj.*) immature and overconfident; conceited
Adolescents aren't the only people whose behavior might at times be considered a bit _____.
SYNONYMS: pretentious, superficial, fatuous
ANTONYMS: mature, judicious, knowledgeable

20. spontaneous
(spän tā' nē əs)

(*adj.*) arising naturally; not planned or engineered in advance
Actors try to make their performances seem as _____ as possible.
SYNONYMS: unpremeditated, unplanned, impromptu
ANTONYMS: premeditated, planned, contrived

Choosing the Right Word

Select the **boldface** word that better completes each sentence. You might refer to the selection on pages 108–109 to see how most of these words are used in context.

1. George Gershwin's early songs gave only a dim (**inkling, deviation**) of the genius that was to express itself in *Porgy and Bess.*

2. During the depression of the 1930s, the nation seemed to take strength from President Roosevelt's (**poignant, copious**) energy and enthusiasm.

3. We must show understanding and acceptance of those who (**exult, deviate**) somewhat from our own standards of what is appropriate.

4. He seems to feel that it is his mission in life to (**chastise, exult**) all those who fail to live up to his standards.

George Gershwin wrote *Of Thee I Sing,* the first musical comedy to win a Pulitzer Prize.

5. Since their loud talk and crude manners were anything but (**palatable, limpid**) to me, I politely declined their invitation to dine with them.

6. He tries hard to sound well-informed, but his superficial answers only betray his (**poignant, sophomoric**) knowledge of world affairs.

7. Your (**ardent, brash**) interest in ecology shows that you care deeply about the welfare of this planet.

8. To make an impression on his fiancée, the young man saved his money to purchase a large faceted diamond that was sparkling and (**limpid, gnarled**).

9. Your simple, (**spontaneous, capricious**) expression of appreciation meant more to me than all the elaborate, carefully phrased tributes I received.

10. Most of the poetry written by the students was (**assiduous, poignant**), filled with powerful imagery that conveyed a surprising depth of emotion.

11. Our meeting last week was marred by a heated debate over how to (**allocate, chastise**) the funds in this year's budget.

12. Though Mom acted surprised, I think she had an (**allocation, inkling**) that we were going to throw her a surprise birthday party.

13. The lecturer explained that the UN is not (**palatable, omnipotent**) and that it can do only what the member states allow it to do.

14. In the concentration camps, the liberating troops found thousands of victims horribly (**ardent, emaciated**) as the result of starvation.

15. Perhaps you have been treated unfairly, but what good will it do to allow your sense of (**indemnity, rancor**) to control your mood and behavior?

16. The destruction wrought by a nuclear war would be so vast that any form of (**inkling, indemnity**) to the injured would be impossible.

17. During the scene in which the deer returns to the forest, leaving the young boy behind, our eyes filled with (**brash, copious**) tears.

18. Lord Tennyson, the poet, speaks of "sorrow's crown of sorrow," by which he means the (**copious, poignant**) experience of remembering happier times.

19. Far from being effortless, her simple, (**limpid, capricious**) writing style is the result of the most painstaking effort.

20. The tastes of the TV audience are so (**capricious, gnarled**) that no one can predict in advance which programs will be successful.

21. She was (**assiduous, brash**) enough to tell her mother she was going to the dance in spite of the doctor's orders.

22. What she lacks in skill, she makes up for in (**assiduous, spontaneous**) attention to every last detail and requirement of the job.

23. The entire student body (**allocated, exulted**) when our team finally won the citywide basketball championship after years of losing to our bitter rivals.

24. I spent the better part of an hour trying to untangle a badly (**gnarled, assiduous**) heap of cables and electrical cords.

25. My sister views my interest in horror films as (**deviate, omnipotent**) behavior.

Synonyms

*Choose the word from this unit that is the same or most nearly the same in meaning as the **boldface** word or expression in the phrase. Write that word on the line. Use a dictionary if necessary.*

1. asked **impertinent** questions _____

2. **restitution** equal to our loss _____

3. a **bittersweet** tale of love and loss _____

4. **apportioned** supplies to each member of the group _____

5. **celebrated** the news from the front _____

6. **crooked** and weather-beaten fingers _____

7. **zealous** supporters of liberty _____

8. the survivors' **gaunt** faces _____

9. **juvenile** literary style _____

10. could find nothing **delectable** on the menu _____

Antonyms

*Choose the word from this unit that is most nearly opposite in meaning to the **boldface** word or expression in the phrase. Write that word on the line. Use a dictionary if necessary.*

1. acting **like a grown-up** _____

2. paid a **penalty for damages** _____

3. a **cautious** investigator _____

4. **steadfast** in one's affections _____

5. **hoarding** supplies in case of an emergency _____

Completing the Sentence

From the words in this unit, choose the one that best completes each of the following sentences. Write the word in the space provided.

1. Under the American system of separation of powers, no government official or agency can ever become _____.

2. We were fascinated to see the consummate grace and skill with which the _____ hands of the old carpenter manipulated his tools.

3. When he told me that he was reading *Huckleberry Finn* for the ninth time, I realized that he was indeed a(n) _____ admirer of the novel.

4. How can you say that the audience's reaction was _____ when the director held up a sign reading "Applause"?

5. If you were as _____ in studying foreign affairs as you are in memorizing batting averages, you would have known how to reply to her comments on the situation in the Middle East.

6. Far from being _____, the director's casting choices were based on a solid appreciation of each actor's abilities and limitations.

7. _____ is never so bitter as when it arises among people who were once close friends.

8. Friends and relatives can be counted on to give _____ amounts of advice on child rearing to the parents of a new baby.

9. Somewhere in a(n) _____ pool in the Canadian Rockies is the large trout that will someday grace the wall of my den.

10. Wasn't it rather _____ of you to offer the soccer coach advice on your very first day as a candidate for the team?

11. Remembering my old friend as a robust 200-pounder, I was shocked to see how _____ he had become during his long illness.

12. As the speaker's voice droned on endlessly in the hot, crowded room, I suddenly realized that I hadn't the slightest _____ of what he was saying.

13. Nothing can arouse _____ memories of long ago and far away like an old, well-loved song!

14. It is of no use to _____ my little brother for not keeping his room clean—he simply refuses to be tidy no matter how much he is scolded.

15. Some of my friends are mentally rather mature for their age; others are of a decidedly _____ turn of mind.

16. If you wish to recover quickly, you must not _____ in the slightest from the doctor's instructions.

17. The teacher decided to _____ a corner of the classroom for an exhibition of student science projects.

18. My travels have shown me that many exotic foods I once considered disgusting are really quite _____ .

19. There can be no _____ for the pain and suffering that your carelessness has caused me!

20. General Grant accepted Lee's surrender with quiet dignity, refusing to _____ over the defeat of a worthy foe.

Writing: Words in Action

1. Look back at "My Last Day in Pompeii" (pages 108–109). Write a brief encyclopedia entry about the eruption of Vesuvius. Base your account on information from the diary entry, but present the information in an objective rather than subjective way, writing from the third-person point of view. Include just the facts, without personal opinions or observations. Support your account using at least two details from the passage and three unit words.

2. Natural disasters, from tsunamis and tornadoes to flooding and drought, continue to disrupt the lives of people all over the world. Imagine that you are the head of a nonprofit organization that supplies aid during times of natural disasters. Write a letter to high school students, explaining some of the ways they, their families, and their friends can help when natural disasters strike. Use your own personal knowledge, studies, and the reading (pages 108–109) to provide ideas and details for your letter. Write at least three paragraphs, and use three or more words from this unit.

Vocabulary in Context

Literary Text

The following excerpts are from The Last of the Mohicans *by James Fenimore Cooper. Some of the words you have studied in this unit appear in **boldface** type. Complete each statement below the excerpt by circling the letter of the correct answer.*

1. "I trust in Heaven you have not **deviated** a single foot from the direct line of our course with so slight a reason!"

   If someone has **deviated** from a course, he has
   a. adhered to it   **c.** divided it
   b. strayed from it   **d.** ruined it

2. A ragged oak...had inclined so far forward that its upper branches overhung that arm of the stream which flowed nearest to its own shore. Among the topmost leaves, which scantily concealed the **gnarled** and stunted limbs, [the enemy] was nestled, partly concealed by the trunk of the tree, and partly exposed, as though looking down upon them to ascertain the effect produced by his treacherous aim.. . .

   Branches that are **gnarled** are
   a. smooth   **c.** crooked
   b. straight   **d.** small

3. The land had been cleared of wood for a reasonable distance around the work, but every other part of the scene lay in the green livery of nature, except where the **limpid** water mellowed the view....

   Water that is NOT **limpid** is
   a. serene   **c.** clear
   b. unclouded   **d.** clouded

The 1992 movie of *The Last of the Mohicans* starred Daniel Day-Lewis.

4. … a frightful stillness succeeded the explosion, which had just been heard bursting from the bowels of the rock. But when Le Renard raised his voice in a long and intelligible whoop, it was answered by a **spontaneous** yell from the mouth of every Indian within hearing of the sound.

   A **spontaneous** yell is
   a. impulsive   **c.** piercing
   b. rehearsed   **d.** gradual

5. "That I cannot see the sunny side of the picture of life, like this artless but **ardent** enthusiast," she added, laying her hand lightly, but affectionately, on the arm of her sister, "is the penalty of experience, and, perhaps, the misfortune of my nature."

   Someone who is **ardent** is
   a. detached   **c.** melancholy
   b. passionate   **d.** insensitive

Interactive Quiz

Snap the code, or go to
vocabularyworkshop.com

Vocabulary for Comprehension

*Read the following selection in which some of the words you have studied in Units 7–9 appear in **boldface** type. Then answer the questions on page 119.*

According to one historian, "When California discovered gold, the world discovered California." The following passage is about the California gold rush.

(Line)

In 1848, a few nuggets of gold were discovered near a sawmill in the Sacramento Valley. News of this discovery set off a rush of gold

(5) seekers to the thinly populated California territory.

As the word of gold spread, **brash** individuals began arriving from all over the globe. Known as *forty-*

(10) *niners* because most of them arrived in 1849, these immigrants left homes, families, and jobs in hopes of staking a claim to a piece of California that would yield gold. They

(15) came by ship, landing in the port of San Francisco, and by covered wagon across the Oregon and California trails. Few had any **inkling** of the difficulties they would face. Yet

(20) no amount of hardship seemed to dim their dreams. By the end of 1849, this **spontaneous** influx of people had increased California's population from about 15,000 to

(25) 100,000. The territory was admitted to the Union in 1850.

Such rapid growth brought **chaos** as well as prosperity to the new state. Once-small towns such as San

(30) Francisco and Sacramento suddenly grew large and wealthy by catering

to the needs of the prospectors. It took a while for this newfound wealth to be put to good civic use.

(35) Numerous camp towns also grew up overnight near the mines. These were generally **squalid**, lawless settlements that often disappeared as quickly as they appeared if the

(40) veins of gold went dry.

Although some forty-niners did strike it rich, the majority found themselves with small holdings that yielded a **parsimonious** living in

(45) return for very hard labor. Many would-be gold miners also ended up working for small wages in large mines owned by others. Still others had to turn to farming or ranching to

(50) support themselves. For many individuals, the California gold rush was a disappointment or a disaster. But for California itself, it was a boon, providing the fledgling state with

(55) new sources of wealth, transportation, and political influence.

1. The main purpose of the passage is to
   a. describe the population of California
   b. provide a brief history of California
   c. examine the causes of the gold rush
   d. evaluate the impact of the gold rush
   e. discuss the experiences of the forty-niners

2. The meaning of **brash** (line 7) is
   a. brave
   b. rash
   c. young
   d. industrious
   e. hopeful

3. **Inkling** (line 18) most nearly means
   a. notion
   b. experience
   c. theory
   d. news
   e. map

4. **Spontaneous** (line 22) is best defined as
   a. desperate
   b. gigantic
   c. memorable
   d. premeditated
   e. unplanned

5. The statistics in lines 22–26 provide evidence of the
   a. transformation of small towns in California
   b. diversity of the population of California
   c. rush of gold seekers to California
   d. growth of industry in California
   e. size of the California territory

6. The meaning of **chaos** (line 27) is
   a. poverty
   b. turmoil
   c. change
   d. peace
   e. civilization

7. **Squalid** (line 37) most nearly means
   a. temporary
   b. ordinary
   c. sordid
   d. joyless
   e. small

8. **Parsimonious** (line 44) is best defined as
   a. meager
   b. comfortable
   c. lavish
   d. average
   e. welcome

9. The 1848 discovery of gold in the Sacramento Valley led to all of the following EXCEPT
   a. statehood for California
   b. the fulfillment of dreams
   c. immigration from all over the world
   d. fabulous wealth for most forty-niners
   e. the death of dreams

10. The author uses the last two sentences of the passage (lines 50–57) to
    a. discourage risk taking
    b. memorialize the forty-niners
    c. put the gold rush in perspective
    d. promote tourism to California
    e. encourage would-be gold seekers

11. The legacy of the gold rush can best be described as
    a. clearly significant
    b. almost negligible
    c. largely negative
    d. totally positive
    e. rather vague

12. The author of the passage would probably agree with which of the following statements?
    a. Were it not for the gold rush, California would never have been admitted to the Union.
    b. Gold mining is an easy way to acquire a fortune.
    c. The impact of the gold rush on California cannot be overstated.
    d. The journey to California was the best part of the gold rush experience.
    e. Were it not for the gold rush, California would be a richer state today.

Two-Word Completions

Select the pair of words that best complete the meaning of each of the following passages.

1. I hoped that my project proposal would be hailed by my classmates with
_____ enthusiasm. Instead, it was greeted with "deafening"
_____.
   a. sophomoric . . . indemnity
   b. compatible . . . animosity
   c. vociferous . . . apathy
   d. copious . . . chaos

2. Infuriated by their treacherous behavior, the enraged party leader severely
_____ the _____ who had unexpectedly bolted
to the opposition during the crucial vote.
   a. chastised . . . renegades
   b. consecrated . . . deviates
   c. implicated . . . martinets
   d. derided . . . revelers

3. "My years of foreign service have taught me to be as _____ as
possible," the veteran diplomat observed, his tongue firmly in his cheek. "These
days, turning up one's nose at another country's national dish, no matter how
_____, might just trigger a very unpleasant international incident."
   a. recalcitrant . . . disingenuous
   b. suave . . . chaotic
   c. compatible . . . squalid
   d. omnivorous . . . unpalatable

4. Though I am perfectly willing to give praise where I feel praise is due, I refuse to
_____ an action that I consider underhanded and
_____.
   a. abhor . . . extant
   b. commend . . . reprehensible
   c. deride . . . sophomoric
   d. amend . . . apprehensive

5. As the storm's intensity increased, the calm waters of the lake became more and
more _____. Strong gusts of wind slapped at our sails, and our
tiny craft was _____ about like a golf ball in an electric blender.
   a. turbulent . . . buffeted
   b. voluminous . . . deviated
   c. vociferous . . . waived
   d. capricious . . . derided

6. The soldiers who fell in the engagement were _____ in a portion
of the battlefield on which they had fought. The spot where they were laid to rest
was not technically "hallowed ground." Still, it was considered appropriate because
they had, in effect, _____ it with their blood.
   a. discerned . . . commended
   b. chastised . . . waived
   c. interred . . . consecrated
   d. implicated . . . buffeted

7. It would be impossible for a career to _____ a person as dynamic
and unstoppable as Claire. She has such _____ talents that, if she
felt bored or unchallenged by one job, she could readily turn to another occupation.
   a. obviate . . . spontaneous
   b. chastise . . . capricious
   c. implicate . . . parsimonious
   d. stultify . . . multifarious

Idioms

In the essay about Emmeline Pankhurst (see pages 88–89), the author writes that Pankhurst liked to "shake things up"—an idiom that means "to create changes" or "to challenge the status quo." The idiom tells us that Pankhurst actively worked to bring about change.

An **idiom** is an expression, often a figure of speech, that conveys an action or idea in a colorful, clever way. Idiomatic expressions are important to everyday language, creating memorable images and serving as a kind of "shorthand" for getting meanings across. Idioms cannot be taken literally and may be hard to interpret if you try to simply analyze the meaning of each individual word. That is why it can be useful to memorize the meanings of common idioms.

Choosing the Right Idiom

Read each sentence. Use context clues to figure out the meaning of each idiom in **boldface** *print. Then write the letter of the definition for the idiom in the sentence.*

1. When you move, you have to **get your ducks in a row**: pack, hire a mover, close your bank account, cancel your utilities, and fill out change of address forms. _____

2. Andre always starts working on his reports **at the eleventh hour**; then he wonders why he gets so stressed. _____

3. My four-year-old sister talks all the time and just **drives me up a wall**. _____

4. Of course I know what Marisa scored on the test; I just heard it **straight from the horse's mouth**. _____

5. After Abe dropped the football five times, the coach really **chewed him out**. _____

6. It's your first day at work, so I am assigning Jade to **show you the ropes**. _____

7. I've been on **pins and needles** waiting to find out how I did on the SAT. _____

8. The doctor reported that the hit-and-run victim is recovering, but she is still not **out of the woods**. _____

9. Why don't you just **cut to the chase** and tell me why you won't come to my party? _____

10. I heard you were **in hot water** when your father found out you borrowed the car without asking. _____

a. from the most reliable authority; from a firsthand source

b. free from danger

c. get to the point quickly

d. feeling very nervous

e. become well organized

f. yelled at and criticized

g. provide basic instruction

h. irritates or annoys

i. in serious trouble

j. at the last possible minute

Writing with Idioms

Find the meaning of each idiom. (Use an online or print dictionary if necessary.) Then write a sentence for each idiom.

1. blue in the face

_____

2. the whole nine yards

_____

3. bundle up

_____

4. a dime a dozen

_____

5. burn the midnight oil

_____

_____

6. spill the beans

_____

_____

7. at sixes and sevens

_____

_____

8. in the bag

_____

9. drawing a blank

_____

10. feet on the ground

_____

11. steal your thunder

_____

12. go out on a limb

_____

Denotation and Connotation

A word's dictionary definition is its **denotation**—a formal, literal meaning of the word. However, many words also have emotional associations, or meanings that people attach to them.

The emotional associations that people make to words are called **connotations**. A word's connotation, its implied meaning, can be quite powerful.

Consider these synonyms for the word *sad*:

poignant   *melancholy*   *somber*   *gloomy*

These four words all have strong connotations. *Poignant* has a positive connotation; a *poignant* movie touches the emotions deeply. *Melancholy* has a more negative connotation, suggesting a mood of sadness. *Somber* and *gloomy* have the most negative connotations of all, referring to depressed and disheartened states of mind.

> **Think:** *Poignant* or *melancholy* music can stir up feelings that are pleasurably sad and touching, while *somber* or *gloomy* music can make a person feel depressed and miserable.

Look at these examples of words that are similar in denotation but have different connotations.

NEUTRAL	POSITIVE	NEGATIVE
acidic	sharp	corrosive
economical	thrifty	parsimonious
thin	slender	emaciated

Political writers and advertisers, among others, understand the power of strongly connotative words, known as **loaded words**. Knowing how to recognize loaded words can help you interpret the media messages you receive as a citizen and a consumer.

Shades of Meaning

Write a plus sign (+) in the box if the word has a positive connotation. Write a minus sign (–) if the word has a negative connotation. Put a zero (0) if the word is neutral.

1. martinet ☐   **2.** derided ☐   **3.** exulted ☐   **4.** sophomoric ☐

5. copious ☐   **6.** suave ☐   **7.** consecrate ☐   **8.** assiduous ☐

9. omnipotent ☐   **10.** amend ☐   **11.** quandary ☐   **12.** allocate ☐

13. ardent ☐   **14.** gnarled ☐   **15.** commodious ☐   **16.** apathy ☐

Expressing the Connotation

Read each sentence. Select the word in parentheses that expresses the connotation (positive, negative, or neutral) given at the beginning of the sentence.

positive **1.** Audiences always seem to (**carouse, revel**) in the high-spirited jazz-blues compositions that my uncle's jazz ensemble performs.

positive **2.** The crab cakes they serve at the old diner near the wharf are (**palatable, scrumptious**).

negative **3.** The hikers found refuge from the thunderstorm in a (**neglected, squalid**) old barn.

positive **4.** We went to express our (**pity, condolences**) and offer our support to the bereaved couple.

neutral **5.** The children were (**chastised, admonished**) when they ran into the house with muddy shoes.

positive **6.** Beneath the (**limpid, transparent**) surface of the pond I could see several large orange and white koi fish idly floating.

positive **7.** Herding livestock with a (**recalcitrant, determined**) cattle dog can give a person quite a workout!

neutral **8.** My older brother refuses to believe that CDs and DVDs will soon be (**obsolete, outdated**).

Challenge: Using Connotation

Choose vocabulary words from Units 7–9 to replace the highlighted words in the sentences below. Then explain how the connotation of the replacement word changes the tone of the sentence.

vociferous	ingenuous	martinet
obsolete	voluminous	compatible

1. My cousin is a **loud** _____ critic of social policies that have a negative impact on lower-income communities.

_____

_____

2. If you get Ms. Wooten as your ballet instructor, watch out: She is a real **disciplinarian** _____!

_____

_____

3. My little sister's upper body was completely engulfed by the **huge** _____ pink parka.

_____

_____

Classical Roots

voc, vok—to call

This root appears in **vociferous**, "loud or noisy" (page 92). Some other words based on the same root are listed below.

advocate	**convocation**	**evoke**	**revoke**
avocation	**equivocal**	**invoke**	**vocalize**

From the list of words above, choose the one that corresponds to each of the brief definitions below. Write the word in the blank space in the illustrative sentence below the definition. Use an online or print dictionary if necessary.

1. to plead in favor of; one who defends a cause; one who pleads the cause of another

Our senators _____ reform of the tax code.

2. a meeting, especially of members of a college or clergy (*"a calling together"*)

The president will attend the _____ of world leaders.

3. an occupation or activity pursued for enjoyment, in addition to one's regular work; a hobby

Bird-watching can be a lifelong _____.

4. to call in for help or support; to appeal to as an authority; to put into effect; to make an earnest request for (*"to call on"*)

The lawyer tried to _____ the sympathy of the jurors.

5. open to two or more interpretations, ambiguous; uncertain or doubtful in nature

The reporter's pointed question drew an _____ response from the candidate.

6. to call forth; bring to mind (*"to call out"*)

The tone poem *La Mer* _____ the sounds of the sea.

7. to give voice to; to sing without words

Therapists encourage their patients to _____ their hopes and fears.

8. to bring or call back; to annul by recalling

A judge can _____ the license of a driver who has a record of repeated violations.

Read the following selection, taking note of the **boldface** words and their contexts. These words are among those you will be studying in Unit 10. As you complete the exercises in this unit, it may help to refer to the way the words are used below.

Hakoah Athletes: From Strength to Victory
<Historical Nonfiction>

By the mid-1930s, while swimmer Judith Deutsch was still an Austrian teenager, the **sinuous** freestyle form that she brought to competition had enabled her to claim every women's middle- and long-distance record in her country. She was awarded Austria's prestigious Golden Badge of Honor in 1936. It was not a surprise, then, when Deutsch was chosen to represent her nation in that year's Summer Olympics in Berlin; the surprise was that Deutsch refused to compete at those games. The **allure** of Olympic gold had a less powerful hold on her than the Jewish athlete's moral convictions. "I refuse to enter a contest in a land which so shamefully persecutes my people," she stated, publicly protesting the German Nazis' politics of hatred.

The pressure on the 17-year-old swimmer was enormous, but Deutsch refused to **acquiesce**. Calm and displaying a **sonorous**

dignity when she spoke, she stood firm in her protest against the treatment of Jews by Germany's new führer, Adolph Hitler, thus infuriating the Nazis allied with Germany. In **retribution**, the Austrian government banished Deutsch from all competition. Soon, the Austrian authorities expunged her many victories from their record books as well. In an abhorrent time, hers was a righteous human act.

To those who believe there's no education like adversity, it would seem fitting that Deutsch got her athletic training from an organization founded as a bulwark against prejudice. Hakoah was a Jewish sports club started in Vienna in 1909, a time of **contentious** Aryan Laws that barred organizations from including Jewish participants. The founders of Hakoah were **exponents** of political views **professed** by the Hungarian social critic Max Nordau. He believed that "muscular Judaism" was a way to

Judith Deutsch as a 17 year-old swimmer

The Hakoah swim team with their coach

challenge the widely held image of the intellectual but physically weak Jew. The name chosen for the sports organization, *Hakoah*, was thus no **misnomer**. The word means "strength." Hakoah encouraged its members to train vigorously in order to demolish this damaging stereotype. Respect, as much as winning, is what its athletes **coveted**.

Hakoah Vienna grew rapidly, and by the 1920s, it had become one of Austria's largest sports clubs. Members found there not only a stage upon which to exhibit their athletic prowess, but also a **respite** from the growing anti-Semitism of their time. As a result, Hakoah was in the **vanguard** of community and civil rights groups, serving as a model for the many that followed.

Judith Deutsch is only one of Hakoah Vienna's success stories. Many other club athletes ranked among the finest in early 20th century Europe. Consider the 1923 men's soccer team. Its players traveled to England and defeated the fierce West Ham United players. If the humbled West Ham athletes and their fans were **crestfallen**, the victorious Jewish players were jubilant; they became the first visiting team to defeat a British squad on its own soil. Two years later, the same team won Austria's national championship. And at the 1932 Olympics in Los Angeles, Hakoah wrestler Micky Hirschl earned two medals.

After the Nazi takeover of Austria in 1938, life for Jews in Vienna became untenable as the Nazis intensified their anti-Semitic campaign. Hakoah Vienna was forced to disband. Friendships and connections forged during the club's heyday enabled many of its members to flee what was first seen as **lamentable**, then became deadly, persecution. A tip from Hakoah's swim-team president, for example, saved the life of a young swimmer named Fred Marcus. After escaping the Nazis, Marcus was placed aboard a ship, alone, to Uruguay. There he became a celebrated swimming and diving champion before emigrating to the United States.

Watermarks, a documentary film from 2004, examines the rise and fall of Hakoah Vienna and its athletes. The poignant return to the pool, where Deutsch and other members of the women's swim team had once **blithely** spent many youthful hours, shows the emotional reunion, after 65 years apart, of many of these extraordinary athletes. In celebrating both the athletes and the organization that brought them together at a dangerous time in history, the film is a powerful tribute, one that is more lasting than any medal or trophy.

iWords

Snap the code, or go to
vocabularyworkshop.com

The Hakoah men's soccer team, 1928

Definitions

Note the spelling, pronunciation, part(s) of speech, and definition(s) of each of the following words. Then write the word in the blank spaces in the illustrative sentence(s) following. Finally, study the lists of synonyms and antonyms.

1. acquiesce
(ak wē es')

(*v.*) to accept without protest; to agree or submit

Management is not likely to _____ to union demands for raises because the company's profits have recently been on the decline.

SYNONYMS: comply with, accede, consent, yield
ANTONYMS: resist, protest

2. allure
(a lür')

(*v.*) to entice, tempt; to be attractive to; (*n.*) a strong attraction; the power to attract, charm

Dreams of stardom _____ many gifted young performers from all over the country to the bright lights of Broadway.

The _____ of get-rich-quick schemes may lead people down the road to financial ruin.

SYNONYMS: (*v.*) beguile, tantalize; (*n.*) temptation, enticement
ANTONYMS: (*v.*) repel, turn off; (*n.*) repellent

3. askew
(ə skyü')

(*adj., adv.*) twisted to one side, crooked; disapprovingly

Some people cannot refrain from straightening lampshades that are a little _____.

All our plans for a picnic on the beach went suddenly _____ when it began to rain very heavily.

SYNONYMS: awry, lopsided, cockeyed
ANTONYMS: straight, symmetrical

4. blithe
(blīth)

(*adj.*) cheerful, lighthearted; casual, unconcerned

It is difficult to deflate the _____ optimism of the young.

SYNONYMS: carefree, nonchalant, indifferent
ANTONYMS: glum, morose, despondent, depressed

5. contentious
(kən ten' shəs)

(*adj.*) quarrelsome, inclined to argue

The members of the on-line discussion group were annoyed by the newcomer's _____ and rude remarks.

SYNONYMS: argumentative, disputatious, combative
ANTONYMS: agreeable, amiable, affable, pacific

6. covet
(kəv' ət)

(*v.*) to desire something belonging to another

Those who _____ the good fortune of others are likely to be unhappy with their own lot in life.

SYNONYMS: crave, yearn for, hunger for
ANTONYMS: disdain, scorn, despise

7. crestfallen
(krest' fô lən)

(*adj.*) discouraged, dejected, downcast

Despite the loss of an important labor endorsement, the candidate appeared in no way _____.

SYNONYMS: despondent, disconsolate
ANTONYMS: elated, cheerful, self-satisfied, cocky

8. disheveled
(di shev' əld)

(*adj.*) rumpled, mussed; hanging in disorder

Most people look a little bit _____ when they get up in the morning.

SYNONYMS: untidy, disarranged, tousled
ANTONYMS: tidy, well-groomed

9. exponent
(ek spō' nənt)

(*n.*) one who advocates, speaks for, explains, or interprets; (*math*) the power to which a number, symbol, or expression is to be raised

President Theodore Roosevelt was one of the first _____ of conservation.

In the equation $x^2 + y^2 = z^2$, the small raised 2s are all _____.

SYNONYMS: defender, champion, interpreter
ANTONYMS: critic, adversary, faultfinder, detractor

10. garrulous
(gar' ə ləs)

(*adj.*) given to much talking, tediously chatty

If you are conversing with a _____ individual, you may find it hard to get a word in edgewise.

SYNONYMS: talkative, loquacious
ANTONYMS: reticent, mum, taciturn, laconic

11. insuperable
(in sü' pər ə bəl)

(*adj.*) incapable of being overcome

To the composer Ludwig van Beethoven, increasing deafness was not an _____ handicap.

SYNONYMS: invincible, insurmountable
ANTONYMS: surmountable, conquerable

12. lamentable
(lam' ən tə bəl)

(*adj.*) to be regretted or pitied

After a long, hard winter, city streets may be in a truly _____ state of disrepair.

SYNONYMS: deplorable, regrettable, distressing
ANTONYMS: praiseworthy, commendable, laudable

13. misnomer
(mis nō' mər)

(*n.*) an unsuitable or misleading name

The term *World Series* is a _____ because only North American teams participate in this annual event.

SYNONYMS: misnaming, malapropism

14. profess
(prə fes')

(*v.*) to affirm openly; to state belief in; to claim, pretend

My music teacher _____ herself satisfied with my technical progress so far this year.

SYNONYMS: assert, proclaim, purport
ANTONYMS: disclaim, disavow, repudiate

15. respite
(res' pit)

(*n.*) a period of relief or rest

A vacation provides a _____ from the worries and responsibilities of everyday life.

SYNONYMS: interval, intermission, lull, breather

16. retribution
(re trə byü' shən)

(*n.*) a repayment; a deserved punishment

In most ancient societies _____ was swiftly visited on those who broke their promises.

SYNONYMS: recompense, requital, just deserts

17. sinuous
(sin' yü əs)

(*adj.*) winding, having many curves; lithe and flexible

The trunk of the tree was almost completely encased by _____ wisteria vines.

SYNONYMS: twisting, convoluted, supple
ANTONYMS: direct, unbending, stiff, rigid

18. sonorous
(sə nōr' əs)

(*adj.*) full, deep, or rich in sound; impressive in style

The _____ tolling of church bells announced the passing of the monarch.

SYNONYMS: resonant, resounding, grandiloquent
ANTONYMS: tinny, reedy, harsh, grating

19. vanguard
(van' gärd)

(*n.*) the foremost part of an army; the leading position in any field

If a high-tech company is to survive in today's marketplace, it must remain in the _____ of innovation.

SYNONYMS: forefront, cutting edge, trailblazers
ANTONYMS: rear guard, stragglers, laggards

20. wastrel
(wās' trəl)

(*n.*) a wasteful person, spendthrift; a good-for-nothing

Many a novel has told the sorry tale of a charming but self-destructive _____.

SYNONYMS: loafer, idler, profligate
ANTONYMS: skinflint, tightwad

Choosing the Right Word

Select the **boldface** word that better completes each sentence. You might refer to the selection on pages 126–127 to see how most of these words are used in context.

1. The (**vanguard, allure**) of "gold in them thar hills" brought many immigrants to California in 1849.

2. Walking out on the empty stage and speaking the opening lines of the play seemed a(n) (**covetous, insuperable**) difficulty to the young actors.

3. Anyone who spends hours, days, and weeks just hanging around is a (**wastrel, vanguard**) with the most precious thing we have—*time*.

4. Because it was the duty of town criers to deliver public proclamations, they were often chosen for their (**sonorous, contentious**) voices.

5. After we had been playing our favorite music at top volume for several hours, Mother entered the room and begged for some (**respite, allure**).

During the California Gold Rush, prospectors—called "Forty-niners"— endured many hardships for the promise of striking it rich.

6. Although we really don't agree with Mother's musical taste, we decided to (**profess, acquiesce**) to her appeal.

7. Since Ben was confident he could play varsity ball, he was extremely (**blithe, crestfallen**) when the coach cut him from the squad.

8. With hair styles what they are these days, many men now seem to look somewhat (**disheveled, garrulous**) when they come home fresh from the barber.

9. As I watched the gymnastic meet on TV, nothing impressed me more than the incredibly graceful and (**askew, sinuous**) movements of the athletes.

10. Wasteful use of energy at a time when there is a critical shortage of such resources is indeed (**lamentable, sonorous**).

11. His willingness to experiment with interesting new ideas clearly put him in the (**vanguard, retribution**) of social reform in his time.

12. With her lipstick smeared, her hair disarranged, and her hat (**askew, crestfallen**), she certainly was a strange sight.

13. He is so (**contentious, sinuous**) that if someone says "Nice day," he'll start a full-scale debate on the weather.

14. The poet Shelley, entranced by the joyous song of the skylark, addressed the bird as "(**garrulous, blithe**) spirit."

15. The wicked may seem to prosper, but I am convinced that sometime, somehow, in this life or the next, there will be (**exponents, retribution**).

16. After years of waiting, the affluent collector was able to purchase the (**professed, coveted**) piece of art by Matisse.

17. When we ended up in the lake, we realized that the skipper was not the expert boatman he (**acquiesced, professed**) to be.

18. Seeking (**retribution, respite**) from the cold weather, the hikers entered the cave and immediately built a small fire.

19. The intently longing gaze that he fixed upon my plate told me that Rover (**professed, coveted**) my lunch.

20. It would be a (**misnomer, respite**) to label as biography a book that is clearly a work of fiction, even though its main character is historical.

21. Marshall McLuhan, a leading (**wastrel, exponent**) of TV's importance in modern life, coined the phrase "the medium is the message."

22. She should have known that Andre was a (**wastrel, respite**), unworthy of her attentions, when he announced that he had no interest in holding a job.

23. The taxi driver was so (**lamentable, garrulous**) during the long trip that it was a relief to return to my silent hotel room.

24. The church bells could be heard (**sonorously, contentiously**) ringing through the valley, announcing the end of the war.

25. The (**sinuous, crestfallen**) road to Hana is both unnerving and breathtaking.

Synonyms

*Choose the word from this unit that is the same or most nearly the same in meaning as the **boldface** word or expression in the phrase. Write that word on the line. Use a dictionary if necessary.*

1. a slightly **inappropriate name** _____

2. **payback** for a life of crime _____

3. looking **unkempt** and confused _____

4. the **front line** of medical science _____

5. proved to be something of a **squanderer** _____

6. a **serpentine** river flowing to sea _____

7. a **contradiction** that it is an international airport _____

8. a still-life arrangement that seemed **off-kilter** _____

9. a **long-winded** talk show host _____

10. faced **unbeatable** odds _____

Antonyms

*Choose the word from this unit that is most nearly opposite in meaning to the **boldface** word or expression in the phrase. Write that word on the line. Use a dictionary if necessary.*

1. a **reserved** child _____

2. an **easily overcome** opponent _____

3. an **orderly** arrangement of knickknacks _____

4. the **neat** state of the room _____

5. remembered as a **miser** _____

Completing the Sentence

From the words in this unit, choose the one that best completes each of the following sentences. Write the word in the space provided.

1. It isn't likely that the school administration will _____ to your recommendation to do away with all examinations and grades.

2. Driving a car along those _____ mountain roads at a height of ten thousand feet calls for stronger nerves than I have.

3. You certainly have a right to your opinions, but you have become so _____ that you immediately challenge opinions expressed by anyone else.

4. The _____ personality that had made her so charming and popular was unaffected by the passage of the years.

5. A staunch believer in the equality of the sexes, Susan B. Anthony was one of the most effective _____ of women's rights.

6. Retailers who seek to _____ unwary consumers with false claims should feel the full penalties of the law.

7. Now that the football season has ended, don't you think our school's athletes deserve a brief _____ before beginning basketball practice?

8. After I heard my new parrot's harsh call, I decided that "Melody," the name I had planned for it, was something of a(n) _____.

9. The body of the slain hero was accompanied to its final resting place by the _____ strains of a funeral march.

10. Excessively _____ people usually don't have the imagination to realize that their endless chatter is boring everyone else.

11. I do not _____ to be heroic, but I hope I have the nerve to stand up for unpopular ideas that I believe are right.

12. With the publication of her famous book *Silent Spring*, Rachel Carson moved into the _____ of those seeking to protect our natural environment.

13. The pioneers succeeded in settling the West because they refused to admit that any obstacle, however formidable, was _____.

14. We can all agree that the crime situation in this community is truly _____, but what are we going to do about it?

15. He says that he is spending the family fortune "to promote the art of good living," but I consider him no more than a(n) _____.

16. In spite of her rain-soaked clothing and _____ appearance, it seemed to me that she had never looked lovelier.

17. "The blinds are hanging _____ because the pull cord is all knotted and tangled," I said.

18. For the innumerable crimes and cruelties he had committed, the tyrant had good reason to fear _____.

19. I confess I suffered a twinge of envy when I learned that my rival had won the prize I had _____ so dearly.

20. After all my high hopes, I was utterly _____ when the notice arrived that I had failed my driver's test.

Writing: Words in Action

1. Look back at "Hakoah Athletes: From Strength to Victory" (pages 126–127). Think about Judith Deutsch's hopes and ambitions as an athlete. Do you think she made the right decision by refusing to participate in the Summer Olympics in Berlin? Write a brief essay explaining why or why not. Support your position using at least two details from the passage and three unit words.

2. Spanish philosopher George Santayana once said that people who forget the past repeat mistakes they made in the past. Do you agree or disagree that it is important to remember the past, including horrific events such as the persecution of the Jews by the Nazis? Write a short essay explaining your position. Use your own personal knowledge, current events, and the reading (refer to pages 126–127) to support your assessment. Write at least three paragraphs, and use three or more words from this unit.

Vocabulary in Context

The following excerpts are from Jane Eyre *by Charlotte Brontë. Some of the words you have studied in this unit appear in* **boldface** *type. Complete each statement below the excerpt by circling the letter of the correct answer.*

1. "Mr. Rochester, I must leave you."

"For how long, Jane? For a few minutes, while you smooth your hair—which is somewhat **disheveled**; and bathe your face—which looks feverish?"

Hair that is **disheveled** is

a. coarse   **c.** curly
b. well-groomed   **d.** uncombed

2. The rooks cawed, and **blither** birds sang; but nothing was so merry or so musical as my own rejoicing heart.

Blither birds are

a. joyful   **c.** small
b. unusual   **d.** large

3. ...[H]e was sincerely glad to see his sisters; but in their glow of fervour and flow of joy he could not sympathise. The event of the day—that is, the return of Diana and Mary—pleased him; but the accompaniments of that event, the glad tumult, the **garrulous** glee of reception irked him: I saw he wished the calmer morrow was come.

A **garrulous** reception is NOT

a. lively   **c.** quiet
b. noisy   **d.** exciting

Peggy Ann Garner as the young Jane and Elizabeth Taylor in the 1944 movie of *Jane Eyre*

4. I **coveted** a cake of bread. With that refreshment I could perhaps regain a degree of energy: without it, it would be difficult to proceed. The wish to have some strength and some vigour returned to me as soon as I was amongst my fellow-beings.

Something that is **coveted** is

a. purchased   **c.** requested
b. wanted   **d.** created

5. Mrs. Reed surveyed me at times with a severe eye, but seldom addressed me: since my illness, she had drawn a more marked line of separation than ever between me and her own children.... I felt an instinctive certainty that she would not long endure me under the same roof with her; for her glance, now more than ever, when turned on me, expressed an **insuperable** and rooted aversion.

Something that is **insuperable** is

a. painful   **c.** effortless
b. natural   **d.** unconquerable

Snap the code, or go to
vocabularyworkshop.com

Read the following selection, taking note of the **boldface** words and their contexts. These words are among those you will be studying in Unit 11. As you complete the exercises in this unit, it may help to refer to the way the words are used below.

Should Government Sponsor the Arts?
<Debate>

Members of Alvin Ailey American Dance Theater

Moderator: Today's topic for the debate teams of Central High School and Western High School is this one: *Be it resolved, that government should provide sponsorship of the arts.* Central High is taking the Affirmative, which has first response, and Western High will take the Negative. This debate is being broadcast over local public radio by Central High's student DJs.

Affirmative: Without government subsidies, arts such as regional dance companies, local playhouses, and art institutes face **stark** and unpleasant futures. Museums will be unable to maintain their artistic **integrity** if they have to **placate** wealthy donors who possess a merely **superficial** knowledge of art—or no knowledge at all. Artists could not afford to take the risks that come with new and innovative art forms, and cultural and societal decline will be the inevitable result. Art is the daughter of freedom, and a country should be proud to support it.

Negative: There are many **potent** arguments against government sponsorship of the arts. Our national test scores are far lower than those of other countries with **exemplary** education systems. Government cannot ignore the fact that schools need more funds for math and science programs. It is wrong to take tax money from where it is desperately needed—to fund extra classes and school lunches—and fritter it away on elitist pastimes.

Affirmative: It is difficult to **fathom** what would happen if government withdrew its support. One would have to be **clairvoyant** to foresee all of the consequences. No doubt, museums would have to charge admissions. The opposing side **alluded** to children on school lunches, and those same children might never go to a museum because of the cost. Our shared wealth of culture and beauty would be shut off to the average person—a clear disadvantage to the very people the opposing side wishes to support.

Negative: There are dangers inherent in government subsidies for the arts—and not just the fact that the money might support projects some citizens find **disreputable** and **obnoxious**. History proves that government patronage can backfire if it is just a **pretext** for making artists promote a regime's goals and values. In the past, artists worked to please the monarchs who paid them and, more recently, subsidized artists disseminated the ideologies of tyrants and dictators.

Furthermore, a responsible government should use its limited funds where the needs and **endemic** problems are greatest. The best arts organizations will sustain themselves through the powers of the free market and, if they cannot, they **misconstrue** their importance to society. One example of such a policy is the case of the local public radio station. When government support for this station was withdrawn, listeners contributed money to the station, and it is still on the airways.

Affirmative: It is easy to recognize the connection between defunding the arts and the disintegration of social structure.

The Stuyvesant High School Chamber Choir

Consider the example of one county that cut funding for its after-school choral society. Low-income students who took part in this activity at no cost had higher GPAs than the county's average. When the county defunded the program, 75 percent of the choral members saw their GPAs drop, and some former members were turned down for scholarships they had been on track to receive. This is **conclusive** evidence that supporting the arts is money well spent.

Moderator: Thank you. Our judge will now consider your arguments and determine the winner of today's debate.

Snap the code, or go to
vocabularyworkshop.com

Students work as radio DJs.

Definitions

Note the spelling, pronunciation, part(s) of speech, and definition(s) of each of the following words. Then write the word in the blank spaces in the illustrative sentence(s) following. Finally, study the lists of synonyms and antonyms.

1. allude
(ə lüd′)

(*v.*) to refer to casually or indirectly

In his speech, the candidate _____ to his opponent's lack of military experience.

SYNONYMS: suggest, insinuate, intimate

2. clairvoyant
(klâr voi′ ənt)

(*adj.*) supernaturally perceptive; (*n.*) one who possesses extrasensory powers, seer

Few people are taken in by the _____ pronouncements of fortune-tellers and mediums.

The police sometimes use _____ to help them solve difficult missing-person cases.

SYNONYMS: (*adj.*) insightful, discerning, uncanny; (*n.*) visionary
ANTONYMS: (*adj.*) blind, unseeing, myopic, dense

3. conclusive
(kən klü′ siv)

(*adj.*) serving to settle an issue; final

When they weighed all the evidence in the case, the members of the jury found the testimony of the expert witness to be

_____.

SYNONYMS: decisive, convincing, definitive
ANTONYMS: unsettled, provisional, indefinite

4. disreputable
(dis rep′ yə tə bəl)

(*adj.*) not respectable, not esteemed

Supermarket tabloids frequently publish stories about the _____ behavior of celebrities.

SYNONYMS: disgraceful, discreditable, shady
ANTONYMS: honest, aboveboard, respectable, creditable

5. endemic
(en dem′ ik)

(*adj.*) native or confined to a particular region or people; characteristic of or prevalent in a field

Scientists have yet to identify many plant and animal species _____ to the rain forests.

SYNONYMS: indigenous, restricted to
ANTONYMS: alien, foreign, extraneous

6. exemplary
(eg zem′ plə rē)

(*adj.*) worthy of imitation, commendable; serving as a model

The Medal of Freedom is awarded to U.S. civilians for _____ achievements in various fields.

SYNONYMS: praiseworthy, meritorious, sterling, illustrative
ANTONYMS: infamous, notorious, scandalous, disreputable

7. fathom
(fath′ əm)

(v.) to understand, get to the bottom of; to determine the depth of;
(n.) a measure of depth in water

It is sometimes difficult to _____ the motives behind another person's actions.

The great passenger liner *Titanic* still lies buried several thousand _____ beneath the ocean's surface.

SYNONYMS: (v.) grasp, figure out, plumb

8. guile
(gīl)

(n.) treacherous cunning, deceit

Folklore has it that a serpent's most outstanding trait is _____, just as a fox's is craftiness.

SYNONYMS: trickery, chicanery
ANTONYMS: candor, artlessness, naïveté, plain dealing

9. integrity
(in teg′ rə tē)

(n.) honesty, high moral standards; an unimpaired condition, completeness, soundness

Scholars debated the _____ of the text of a newly discovered poem attributed to Shakespeare.

SYNONYMS: rectitude, probity
ANTONYMS: dishonesty, corruption, turpitude

10. itinerary
(ī tin′ ə rer ē)

(n.) a route of travel; a record of travel; a guidebook

Tour companies regularly provide potential customers with detailed _____ of the trips they offer.

SYNONYMS: schedule, program

11. misconstrue
(mis kən strü′)

(v.) to interpret wrongly, mistake the meaning of

Young children sometimes _____ their parents' motives.

SYNONYMS: misjudge, misinterpret

12. obnoxious
(äb näk′ shəs)

(adj.) highly offensive, arousing strong dislike

The speeches Hitler delivered at the Nuremberg rallies were full of racial slurs and other _____ language.

SYNONYMS: disagreeable, repugnant, hateful, odious
ANTONYMS: agreeable, pleasing, engaging, personable

13. placate
(plā′ kāt)

(v.) to appease, soothe, pacify

Sponsors of the controversial bill modified some of its original provisions in order to _____ the opposition.

SYNONYMS: satisfy, mollify, allay, conciliate
ANTONYMS: vex, irk, provoke, exasperate, annoy

14. placid
(plas' id)

(*adj.*) calm, peaceful

There was no wind to disturb the _____ surface of the lake.

SYNONYMS: undisturbed, tranquil, quiet, serene
ANTONYMS: stormy, agitated, turbulent, tempestuous

15. potent
(pōt' ənt)

(*adj.*) powerful; highly effective

Music has been called the most _____ agent for inducing people to forget their differences and live in harmony.

SYNONYMS: mighty, formidable, forceful
ANTONYMS: weak, inept, feckless, powerless, ineffective

16. pretext
(prē' tekst)

(*n.*) a false reason, deceptive excuse

I sought some _____ for excusing myself from the weekly staff meeting I did not want to attend.

SYNONYMS: pretense, cover story, rationale, evasion

17. protrude
(prō trüd')

(*v.*) to stick out, thrust forth

Dentists commonly use various kinds of braces to correct the alignment of teeth that _____ or are crooked.

SYNONYMS: project, bulge

18. reparation
(rep ə rā' shən)

(*n.*) a payment made for a wrong or an injury

Both Germany and Japan paid _____ to Britain, France, and the United States after WWII.

SYNONYMS: compensation, damages, redress

19. stark
(stärk)

(*adj.*) harsh, unrelieved, desolate; (*adv.*) utterly

Many a young idealist has found it difficult to accept the _____ realities of life.

By the end of his brief reign, the Roman emperor Caligula was clearly _____ raving mad.

SYNONYMS: (*adj.*) sheer, downright, grim, bleak; (*adv.*) absolutely
ANTONYMS: (*adj.*) bright, cheerful, embellished, ornate

20. superficial
(sü pər fish' əl)

(*adj.*) on or near the surface; concerned with or understanding only what is on the surface, shallow

A _____ analysis of a complex problem is not likely to produce a viable or long-lasting solution.

SYNONYMS: skin-deep, insubstantial, cursory, slapdash
ANTONYMS: deep, profound, thorough, exhaustive

Choosing the Right Word

*Select the **boldface** word that better completes each sentence. You might refer to the selection on pages 136–137 to see how most of these words are used in context.*

1. Tom Sawyer used (**guile, integrity**) to get the other boys to do his work by convincing them that whitewashing a fence was fun.

2. Do not be taken in by any (**superficial, conclusive**) resemblances between their half-baked ideas and the sensible program we proposed.

3. Mother was as upset as any of us, but she managed to conceal her fears so that she looked positively (**obnoxious, placid**).

4. If the British government had made a sincere effort to (**placate, misconstrue**) the colonists, would the American Revolution have occurred?

Tom Sawyer represents author Mark Twain's vision of carefree childhood in 1870s Missouri.

5. I find no one more (**obnoxious, clairvoyant**) than a person who insists on talking instead of listening to the brilliant and important things I have to say.

6. When I said you were flying too close to the sun, I was (**placating, alluding**) to the myth about Daedalus and Icarus.

7. Is it any wonder that your parents are worried, knowing that you are associating with such a (**placid, disreputable**) group of people?

8. Modern scientists use all kinds of high-tech gadgetry to (**fathom, allude**) the depths of the ocean.

9. Why not include Mount Vernon in the (**reparation, itinerary**) of our spring vacation?

10. The children cut holes in their paper bag masks to allow for their (**exemplary, protruding**) noses.

11. People with true (**clairvoyance, integrity**) practice their high moral values daily and work to improve their characters.

12. The spectacular remains of that brilliant period stand in (**stark, disreputable**) contrast to the poverty of archaeological finds from previous eras.

13. Although most of us cannot hope to match Mother Teresa's pure idealism, we may regard her noble life as inspiring and (**exemplary, endemic**).

14. In times of crisis, the utmost care must be taken to prevent ordinary military maneuvers from being (**placated, misconstrued**) as hostile acts.

15. Though all the lights were on, the restaurant refused to serve us, using the (**pretext, itinerary**) that it was closed for the evening.

16. Some people maintain that intelligent life must exist elsewhere in the universe, but I firmly believe that it is (**endemic, potent**) to Earth.

17. The agency was created for the sole purpose of providing (**integrity, reparation**) to victims of human rights violations.

18. The prospect of extremely high starting salaries is a (**stark, potent**) argument for pursuing a career in computer science.

19. It is all very well for science fiction writers to speculate, but is there any (**exemplary, conclusive**) evidence that UFOs exist?

20. Marge produced a convenient headache as her (**pretext, itinerary**) for having to leave early.

21. A candidate for the highest office in the land should be, above all, a person of unshakable (**guile, integrity**).

22. Instead of (**alluding, fathoming**) so often to your own achievements and successes, why not wait for other people to mention them?

23. In that neighborhood of small homes, a few massive apartment buildings (**allude, protrude**) like giants set down in a community of dwarfs.

24. With some psychics it is difficult to tell where the (**clairvoyant, itinerary**) leaves off and the con artist begins.

25. Most of his paintings portray (**stark, potent**) and barren desert landscapes.

Synonyms

*Choose the word from this unit that is the same or most nearly the same in meaning as the **boldface** word or expression in the phrase. Write that word on the line. Use a dictionary if necessary.*

1. failed to **comprehend** the severity of the situation   _____

2. deliberately **mistook** my words   _____

3. a hectic **agenda** with no time for relaxation   _____

4. signs that **obtrude** from the front of the building   _____

5. **reimbursement** for the destruction of property   _____

6. **hinted at** the existence of embarrassing secrets   _____

7. could find no plausible **justification** to stay   _____

8. his **unperturbed** and reassuring manner   _____

9. an advantage gained by **duplicity**   _____

10. shellfish **widespread** at the cape   _____

Antonyms

*Choose the word from this unit that is most nearly opposite in meaning to the **boldface** word or expression in the phrase. Write that word on the line. Use a dictionary if necessary.*

1. **wrongs** inflicted during a conflict _____

2. listed **frankness** as a desirable quality _____

3. his **tumultuous** feelings about the reunion _____

4. **spontaneous and unplanned trip** _____

5. look for nails and screws that **recede** _____

Completing the Sentence

From the words in this unit, choose the one that best completes each of the following sentences. Write the word in the space provided.

1. Sherlock Holmes assured Dr. Watson that it was simple deduction, not some _____ faculty, that led him to the document's hiding place.

2. I selected them as my business partners not only because I respect their ability but also because I have unlimited confidence in their character and _____.

3. Although the cut on my arm was bleeding quite heavily, it proved to be quite _____ and required only a tight bandage.

4. Their idea of a(n) _____ student is someone so perfect in so many ways that he or she would be too good to exist.

5. We spent many pleasant hours poring over all kinds of maps and guidebooks, planning the _____ for our trip across the United States.

6. In 1722, Daniel Defoe published his famous account of the _____ history of Moll Flanders.

7. The tapes of the conversations were regarded as _____ proof that the official had been aware of the crime.

8. Legally a defendant is innocent until proven guilty, so do not _____ a refusal to testify as an admission of guilt.

9. When we consider the _____ misery of the last years of his life, we must conclude that he paid in full for all his offenses.

10. Phyllis was too polite to mention John's crude behavior at the party, but she certainly _____ to it when she spoke of "unnecessary unpleasantness."

11. America's most _____ weapon in the struggle for world influence is its great tradition of democracy and freedom.

12. His skillful use of flattery and double-talk to persuade us to agree to his scheme was a typical example of his _____.

13. His conceit and his cold disregard of other people's feelings make him utterly _____!

14. If you allow your foot to _____ into the aisle, someone may trip over it.

15. The man has filed a lawsuit seeking _____ payments on behalf of all families who were forced to live in internment camps.

16. Neither misfortunes nor happy events seem to have the slightest effect on my friend's _____ disposition.

17. Blue jeans, once _____ to the cowboys of the American West, are now a familiar part of the whole world's wardrobe.

18. On the _____ of delivering a package, the burglar sought to gain entrance to the house.

19. By disregarding the flood of excuses, explanations, and justifications, we were able to _____ the true reasons for her actions.

20. It is quite useless to try to _____ dissatisfied customers who actually enjoy being angry and making complaints.

Writing: Words in Action

1. Look back at "Should Government Sponsor the Arts?" (pages 136–137). With which side do you agree—the Affirmative or the Negative? Write an editorial in which you express your opinion about government subsidies for the arts using at least two details from the passage and three unit words.

2. English poet and artist William Blake argued that any limits on artistic expression would destroy a nation and its people. Do you agree with Blake's view of what happens when the arts are restricted in some way? In what ways can the arts be restricted in society? What might be the effects of such restriction? Write a brief essay about this issue, supporting your viewpoint with examples from your studies, the reading (pages 136–137), or your personal experience and observations. Write at least three paragraphs, and use three or more words from this unit.

Vocabulary in Context

Literary Text

The following excerpts are from The Adventures of Sherlock Holmes *by Sir Arthur Conan Doyle. Some of the words you have studied in this unit appear in **boldface** type. Complete each statement below the excerpt by circling the letter of the correct answer.*

1. "'You may as well face the matter,' said I; 'you have been caught in the act, and no confession could make your guilt more heinous. If you but make such **reparation** as is in your power, by telling us where the beryls are, all shall be forgiven and forgotten.'" ("The Adventure of the Beryl Coronet")

   To make a **reparation** is to
   a. offer guidance   **c.** make amends
   b. plead guilty   **d.** provide an alibi

2. For a minute or more the hand, with its writhing fingers, **protruded** out of the floor. Then it was withdrawn as suddenly as it appeared.... ("The Red-Headed League")

   Something that has **protruded**
   a. lies still   **c.** drapes over
   b. juts out   **d.** draws back

3. "'It's only Carlo, my mastiff.... Toller lets him loose every night, and God help the trespasser whom he lays his fangs upon. For goodness' sake don't you ever on any **pretext** set your foot over the threshold at night, for it's as much as your life is worth.'" ("The Adventure of the Copper Beeches")

   Another way to say "on any **pretext**" is
   a. for any reason   **c.** on any assignment
   b. on any hunch   **d.** for any reward

Jeremy Brett portrayed Sherlock Holmes on television in the 1980s–1990s.

4. "Not only that, but the signature is typewritten. Look at the neat little 'Hosmer Angel' at the bottom. There is a date, you see, but no superscription except Leadenhall Street, which is rather vague. The point about the signature is very suggestive—in fact, we may call it **conclusive**." ("A Case of Identity")

   Proof that is **conclusive** is NOT
   a. credible   **c.** irrefutable
   b. persuasive   **d.** disputable

5. Beside the couch was a wooden chair, and on the angle of the back hung a very seedy and **disreputable** hard-felt hat, much the worse for wear, and cracked in several places. ("The Adventure of the Blue Carbuncle")

   An object that is **disreputable** is
   a. unnecessary   **c.** shabby
   b. evident   **d.** obsolete

Interactive Quiz

Snap the code, or go to
vocabularyworkshop.com

*Read the following selection, taking note of the **boldface** words and their contexts. These words are among those you will be studying in Unit 12. As you complete the exercises in this unit, it may help to refer to the way the words are used below.*

Do Not Forget Our Earliest Cultures

<Letter to the Editor>

To the Editor:

In an otherwise excellent article on early cultures of South America ("South America's Ancient Diversity," April 22), author Rigoberto Ruiz-Nunez ignores the lasting significance of the Aymara people. Although the Aymara Empire collapsed over 1,000 years ago, the Aymara are not an **irrelevant** footnote in the history books today. Their empire once spanned the south-central Andes Mountains, and today, an estimated two million of their descendents live in Bolivia and another 500,000 in Peru. The Aymara have made an **indelible** mark on this region.

Saying that the Aymara suffered during colonization is a **platitude** that explains nothing. Millions of Aymara were **callously** worked to death in Spanish silver mines. The Aymara were forced to **abjure** their

traditional religion and culture, although some practices continued in a **clandestine** way. For almost 500 years, Bolivian leaders showed no **compunction** about the mistreatment of the Aymara. Not until 1952 did Bolivia adopt a more **indulgent** policy, granting the Aymara the same civil rights as other Bolivians.

How did the Aymara survive such adversity? For one thing, there has always been a **tacit** agreement among the Aymara to help members of their community. In times of crisis, the Aymara work together— an arrangement that strengthens the group. In addition, centuries of high-altitude living gave the Aymara extraordinary lung capacity. They could live at elevations that left the colonizers faint—a further challenge to any attempts to **quell** rebellions in Aymara communities.

High in the Andes today, many Aymara continue their **inveterate** traditions, including their reliance on potato farming— they were among the first to cultivate this food—and llama and alpaca herding. Others have settled into modern society with **tangible** results. An Aymara political party sends members to the Bolivian Congress, and Aymara TV shows and music groups are popular. The tourist trade provides a ready market for sought-after Aymara woolen goods and weavings. So more than a millennium after the fall of their **august** empire, the Aymara remain a vibrant people, carrying on age-old traditions while exploring modern possibilities.

The Aymara have their own language—Aymara. Many also speak Spanish.

The Moche civilization arose 2,000 years ago in the river valleys and coastal plain of northern Peru.

Peru

To the Editor:

Your recent article about the diverse peoples who populated early South America gave short shrift to an important ancient culture. The Moche people inhabited the river valleys and coastal plain of northern Peru between AD 100 and AD 800. You rightly note that archaeologists are **elated** by recent discoveries in the region: The sophisticated Moche built pyramids, temples, and irrigation canals and produced extraordinary ceramics and murals. Yet the article offers no **trenchant** explanation for why the Moche "disappeared."

Scholars have long **ruminated** on the causes of the Moche collapse. Evidence from glacial ice cores shows that the area experienced 30 years of flooding followed by 30 years of drought. This weather event, from AD 536–594, could have disrupted the Moche food supply.

Furthermore, Moche leaders were charged with ensuring stable weather through religious practices, and their failure to do so may have destabilized the people's faith in their leadership.

Although the Moche had no known enemies, a few of their later settlements did have fortifications. What was the purpose of these defenses? Perhaps food shortages led to bitter infighting among the Moche. Such **acrid** conflicts could have led to the death of thousands and hastened the civilization's decline. The full story of the Moche collapse may never be known. However, I hope articles such as yours will inspire some of your readers to study this and other ancient civilizations.

Although they had no written language, the Moche people excelled at ceramics.

iWords

Snap the code, or go to
vocabularyworkshop.com

Ruins of a Moche pyramid

Definitions

Note the spelling, pronunciation, part(s) of speech, and definition(s) of each of the following words. Then write the word in the blank spaces in the illustrative sentence(s) following. Finally, study the lists of synonyms and antonyms.

1. abjure
(ab jür′)

(*v.*) to renounce, repudiate under oath; to avoid, shun

Toward the end of Shakespeare's last play, *The Tempest*, the magician Prospero _____ his powers over nature.

SYNONYMS: forswear, retract, abstain from
ANTONYMS: affirm, avow, aver, profess

2. acrid
(ak′ rid)

(*adj.*) harsh in taste or odor; sharp in manner or temper

The _____ stench of a fire lingers in the air long after the flames have been extinguished.

SYNONYMS: irritating, stinging, bitter, caustic
ANTONYMS: gentle, soothing, mild

3. august
(ô gəst′)

(*adj.*) majestic, inspiring admiration and respect

The _____ visages of four of America's great presidents are carved on the face of Mount Rushmore.

SYNONYMS: stately, dignified, exalted, venerable
ANTONYMS: humble, base, mean, lowly, abject

4. callous
(ka′ ləs)

(*adj.*) emotionally hardened, unfeeling

Protesters accused the mayor of _____ indifference to the plight of the homeless.

SYNONYMS: insensitive, unsympathetic, thick-skinned
ANTONYMS: sensitive, compassionate, tenderhearted

5. clandestine
(klan des′ tən)

(*adj.*) secret, concealed; underhanded

During the early stages of the American Revolution, _____ colonial printing presses churned out quantities of anti-British propaganda.

SYNONYMS: covert, furtive, surreptitious, stealthy
ANTONYMS: open, overt, undisguised, aboveboard

6. compunction
(kəm pəŋk′ shən)

(*n.*) remorse, regret

In some religious writings _____ is used as a synonym for *contrition* to express profound regret for one's sins.

SYNONYMS: scruple, qualm, misgiving, contrition
ANTONYMS: shamelessness, insouciance, nonchalance

7. conflagration
(kän flə grā′ shən)

(*n.*) a large destructive fire

A large number of wooden structures quite literally added fuel to the_____ that swept through San Francisco in 1906.

SYNONYMS: holocaust, wildfire
ANTONYM: deluge

8. elated
(i lā′ tid)

(*adj.*, *part.*) in high spirits, jubilant; extremely pleased

_____ fans lined the city's streets to cheer the World Series champions.

SYNONYMS: overjoyed, ecstatic, tickled pink
ANTONYMS: depressed, crestfallen, despondent, blue

9. indelible
(in del′ ə bəl)

(*adj.*) not able to be erased or removed; memorable

The brutal crimes against humanity committed by the Nazis left an _____ stain on the history of the twentieth century.

SYNONYMS: lasting, permanent
ANTONYMS: erasable, impermanent, ephemeral

10. indulgent
(in dəl′ jənt)

(*adj.*) yielding to the wishes or demands of others

A heightened sense of compassion has induced the federal government to adopt a more _____ policy toward illegal aliens.

SYNONYMS: permissive, tolerant, liberal
ANTONYMS: strict, severe, hard-nosed

11. inveterate
(in vet′ ər ət)

(*adj.*) firmly established, long-standing; habitual

It has been claimed that many writers and artists have an _____ hostility to criticism.

SYNONYMS: persisting, chronic, dyed-in-the-wool
ANTONYMS: sporadic, intermittent, occasional

12. irrelevant
(i rel′ ə vənt)

(*adj.*) not to the point, not applicable or pertinent

When you take notes, it's best to record only the main ideas and eliminate all _____ details.

SYNONYMS: inapplicable, immaterial, beside the point
ANTONYMS: pertinent, material, apropos, germane

13. nocturnal
(näk tər′ nəl)

(*adj.*) of or occurring in the night; under cover of darkness

Most _____ creatures have keen eyesight and acute hearing.

SYNONYM: nighttime
ANTONYMS: daytime, diurnal

14. platitude
(plat′ ə tüd)

(*n.*) a commonplace, stale, or trite remark
The sentiments expressed in most greeting cards seldom rise above the level of timeworn _____.
SYNONYMS: cliché, truism, bromide
ANTONYMS: epigram, quip, witticism, bon mot

15. quell
(kwel)

(*v.*) to subdue, put down forcibly
The English poet John Dryden believed that music has the power either to arouse or to _____ strong emotions.
SYNONYMS: pacify, squelch, quash, crush
ANTONYMS: incite, provoke, arouse, foment, stir up

16. quiescent
(kwī es′ ənt)

(*adj.*) inactive; at rest
Although some volcanoes are believed to be truly extinct, many are merely _____.
SYNONYMS: still, inert, motionless, tranquil
ANTONYMS: active, thriving, bustling, volatile

17. ruminate
(rü′ mə nāt)

(*v.*) to meditate, think about at length
In old age many people sadly _____ on mistakes made and opportunities missed.
SYNONYMS: ponder, reflect, mull over, muse

18. tacit
(tas′ it)

(*adj.*) unspoken, silent; implied, inferred
The neighbors had a _____ understanding that they would help each other in an emergency.
SYNONYMS: unexpressed, unvoiced, understood, implicit
ANTONYMS: explicit, express, specific

19. tangible
(tan′ jə bəl)

(*adj.*) capable of being touched; real, concrete
After months of intensive negotiation, diplomats reported that they had made _____ progress toward reaching a settlement of the bitter dispute.
SYNONYMS: perceptible, actual, evident
ANTONYMS: immaterial, imperceptible, insubstantial

20. trenchant
(tren′ chənt)

(*adj.*) incisive, keen; forceful, effective; cutting, caustic; distinct, clear-cut
Scholars consider the _____ satires of Jonathan Swift to be the greatest works of their kind in the English language.
SYNONYMS: penetrating, cutting, telling, acute
ANTONYMS: dull, bland, insipid, vapid, imperceptive

Choosing the Right Word

Select the **boldface** word that better completes each sentence. You might refer to the selection on pages 146–147 to see how most of these words are used in context.

1. Alexander the Great's meteoric career of world conquest made an (**indelible, indulgent**) impression on the thoughts and institutions of antiquity.

2. Taking third place in the hundred-meter dash in the intramural track meet left me satisfied but scarcely (**callous, elated**).

3. Although there was no (**tangible, inveterate**) reason for my alarm, I could not shake off the feeling that something terrible was about to happen.

4. His invariably (**acrid, indulgent**) remarks on the state of the world soon earned him the nickname of "Old Sourpuss."

Alexander the Great, King of Macedonia in the 4th century B.C., conquered the Persian Empire.

5. How will you write your novel if you spend most of your time (**abjuring, ruminating**) about the title?

6. An insightful writer usually has no need to rely on hollow generalities or threadbare (**ruminations, platitudes**).

7. I've noticed that many professional football players become (**irrelevant, tacit**) only a few years after their retirement.

8. As part of the settlement, the company must henceforth (**abjure, quell**) unsubstantiated claims for its product.

9. We hoped that the strange noises outside the tent were merely the foraging sounds of small (**nocturnal, inveterate**) creatures like possums and raccoons.

10. Like so many (**clandestine, inveterate**) pack rats, she has found that great self-discipline is needed to break the cluttering habit.

11. Because their misconduct was clearly deliberate, we have no feelings of (**compunction, platitude**) in sentencing them to ten days of detention.

12. The major powers intervened to prevent the brushfire war from engulfing the entire region in a full-scale (**conflagration, platitude**).

13. The deep-seated resentment of the populace, which had long been (**irrelevant, quiescent**), suddenly blossomed into open rebellion.

14. Millions of Americans were thrilled as they witnessed on TV the simple but (**august, clandestine**) ceremony of the presidential inauguration.

15. We may criticize Americans for many things, but they are never (**elated, callous**) when appeals for help come from distressed people.

16. We should seek not to (**quell, elate**) the idealism and enthusiasm of youth but, rather, to direct those impulses into useful channels.

17. Your (**ruminations, compunctions**) on the meaning of life will just be a waste of time unless they lead to some plans for rational behavior.

18. The old (**compunction, platitude**) "You can't teach an old dog new tricks," is based on the principle that old dogs and people do not learn as well as the young.

19. After listening to the senator's (**trenchant, tacit**) analysis, I have a clearer idea of what is involved and where I should stand on the issue.

20. Just before going to sleep, we set traps to discourage the (**indelible, nocturnal**) raids of the raccoons on our food supply.

21. Since my parents offered no objections, I felt that I had their (**acrid, tacit**) consent to go ahead with my plans for a summer trip to California.

22. Though the anecdote was amusing, it was totally (**callous, irrelevant**) to the matter we were discussing at the moment.

23. The judge has a reputation for being generally (**indulgent, trenchant**), but not when confronting an individual convicted of reckless driving.

24. In these days of presidential primaries, candidates can no longer be chosen at (**august, clandestine**) meetings of a few powerful politicians.

25. In a large city, it is difficult to avoid the (**acrid, august**) smoke emitted from cars.

Synonyms

*Choose the word from this unit that is the same or most nearly the same in meaning as the **boldface** word or expression in the phrase. Write that word on the line. Use a dictionary if necessary.*

1. an **inferno** that destroyed thousands of acres _____

2. when nature is at its most **dormant** _____

3. just one **tired expression** after another _____

4. tried to **suppress** their fears _____

5. saw the actor's **unforgettable** performance _____

6. a creature who **sleeps during the day** _____

7. **delighted** by the day's events _____

8. **lenient** grandparents spoiling grandkids _____

9. **palpable** signs of long neglect _____

10. willingly **recanted** their old beliefs _____

Antonyms

*Choose the word from this unit that is most nearly opposite in meaning to the **boldface** word or expression in the phrase. Write that word on the line. Use a dictionary if necessary.*

1. a **lively** seaport _____

2. the city's **daylight** bustle _____

3. a reputation for being **kind** _____

4. red flag warning about a **flood** _____

5. a pleasant and **fleeting** memory _____

Completing the Sentence

From the words in this unit, choose the one that best completes each of the following sentences. Write the word in the space provided.

1. The years of close association with outstanding teachers had left a(n) _____ mark on the students' characters.

2. The debate was decided in our favor when Carole's _____ rebuttal tore the other side's arguments to pieces.

3. How can we possibly accept the testimony of someone who is known to be a(n) _____ liar?

4. According to legend, Mrs. O'Leary's cow kicked over an oil lamp and started the _____ that consumed four square miles of Chicago in 1871.

5. The fumes released by the volcano were so _____ that they caused great discomfort among people in the nearby villages.

6. Some people are so completely wrapped up in their own concerns that they often seem to be _____ about the feelings of others.

7. There was no _____ evidence of his sincerity, but somehow we were confident that he would do all he could to help us.

8. The documents showed that, years before, the companies had made a(n) _____ agreement to divide the market among them.

9. Though we were angry with each other, we had a(n) _____ agreement to act politely in front of our parents.

10. Abraham Lincoln's plan for reconstruction simply had the former rebels _____ allegiance to the Confederacy and vow to support the Union.

11. I tried to _____ my feeling of panic by assuring myself that there is simply no such thing as a ghost.

12. I have no patience with a(n) _____ parent who gives in to every whim and demand of an undisciplined child.

13. The audience seemed to be stirred by the speaker's remarks, but in my opinion they were no more than a series of _____.

14. Who wouldn't be _____ at winning a huge prize on a television quiz show?

15. In the presence of such a(n) _____ assemblage of spiritual leaders representing all the major beliefs, I felt very humble.

16. The streets seemed safe and familiar during the day, but now we had to face unknown _____ dangers.

17. I stretched out under the old maple tree in the backyard and began to _____ on the strange events of that remarkable day.

18. Your statement may be correct, but since it has no bearing on the point now under discussion, I must reject it as _____.

19. Their behavior was so rude and offensive that I had no _____ about telling them to leave the house.

20. Although the disease had been _____ for several years, the doctors warned her that its symptoms could appear again at any time.

Writing: Words in Action

1. Look back at "Do Not Forget Our Earliest Cultures" (pages 146–147). How are the Aymara similar to and different from the Moche? Write a brief essay comparing and contrasting the two South American peoples. Use at least two details from the passage and three unit words.

2. What can the study of ancient cultures teach us? Write a brief essay explaining why it is important for scholars to continue researching and making discoveries about civilizations that no longer exist. What valuable knowledge can we learn by studying the customs, art, language, music, and inventions of an ancient culture? What important information might we gain by understanding how a civilization died or gradually disappeared? Support your position with examples, studies, the reading (pages 146–147), or personal knowledge. Write at least three paragraphs, and use three or more words from this unit.

Vocabulary in Context
Literary Text

*The following excerpts are from Great Expectations by Charles Dickens. Some of the words you have studied in this unit appear in **boldface** type. Complete each statement below the excerpt by circling the letter of the correct answer.*

1. When I got back to my breakfast in the Boar's coffee-room, I found Mr. Pumblechook conversing with the landlord. Mr. Pumblechook (not improved in appearance by his late **nocturnal** adventure) was waiting for me....

    A **nocturnal** adventure takes place

    a. during the night   **c.** during the day
    b. before dusk   **d.** after breakfast

2. "And couldn't Uncle Pumblechook, being always considerate and thoughtful for us —though you may not think it, Joseph," in a tone of the deepest reproach, as if he were the most **callous** of nephews, "then mention this boy, standing Prancing here"—which I solemnly declare I was not doing—"that I have for ever been a willing slave to?"

    A **callous** person is NOT

    a. cruel   **c.** caring
    b. careful   **d.** thoughtless

3. It revived my utmost indignation to find that she was still pursued by this fellow, and I felt **inveterate** against him. I told her so, and told her that I would spend any money or take any pains to drive him out of that country.

    An **inveterate** feeling toward someone is

    a. inexplicable   **c.** protective
    b. undecided   **d.** entrenched

4. "There's one thing you may be sure of, Pip," said Joe, after some **rumination**, "namely, that lies is lies. Howsever they come, they didn't ought to come, and they come from the father of lies, and work round to the same. Don't you tell no more of 'em, Pip."

John Mills and Valerie Hobson star in the 1946 film adaptation of *Great Expectations.*

    A **rumination** is a(n)

    a. hesitation   **c.** deliberation
    b. relaxation   **d.** investigation

5. ...[H]e took us into another room with a dinner-table for thirty, and in the grate a scorched leaf of a copy-book under a bushel of coal-dust. Having looked at this extinct **conflagration** and shaken his head, he took my order....

    The **conflagration** referred to in this passage is

    a. a dinner table   **c.** a messy area
    b. a burned book   **d.** the grate of a fireplace

Interactive Quiz

Snap the code, or go to
vocabularyworkshop.com

Vocabulary for Comprehension

*Read the following selection in which some of the words you have studied in Units 10–12 appear in **boldface** type. Then answer the questions on page 157.*

The following passage describes the human attempt to exert control over a rapidly running river.

(Line)

The Colorado River rises in the Rocky Mountains of Colorado and runs southwest through five states and part of Mexico. The river travels

(5) through a varied and often **stark** landscape that is notable for many deep gorges and canyons. The longest of these is the Grand Canyon. The Colorado has many

(10) rapids and waterfalls along its course. It is prone to periodic flooding and steady erosion of its banks and riverbed.

In the early 1900s, the Colorado's

(15) floods caused severe damage to agriculture in the Palo Verde and Imperial Valleys of California. Many people regarded the river as their enemy. The need to control and

(20) harness this **potent** force of nature was clear, and the federal government responded. In 1928, Congress passed the Boulder Canyon Project Act. The centerpiece

(25) of this ambitious plan, which also included a hydroelectric power plant and a huge reservoir, was the massive Hoover Dam.

The 726-foot Hoover Dam

(30) **protrudes** high above the surface of the river between Nevada and Arizona. Completed in 1936, it contains 4.5 million cubic yards of concrete, enough to build a two-lane

(35) highway between New York City and San Francisco. The harnessed energy of the water flowing through the turbines of the dam generates millions of kilowatts of electricity. The

(40) **placid** waters of Lake Mead, the huge reservoir created by the dam, are used to irrigate the region. They also provide a variety of recreational opportunities.

(45) Altogether, more than twenty huge dams have been built along the Colorado River system. However, evidence that further intervention in the river's natural cycle is needed is

(50) no longer **conclusive**. Proponents of dams make a strong case for the continuing need to control the power of the Colorado and other rivers. Opponents offer equally **trenchant**

(55) arguments for setting rivers free.

1. The main focus of the passage is on the
   a. politicization of a river
   b. restoration of a river
   c. harnessing of a river
   d. dangers of a river
   e. beauty of a river

2. The author uses the first paragraph (lines 1–13) to
   a. describe an engineering wonder
   b. provide background information
   c. present the main idea
   d. state a position
   e. add human interest

3. In line 5, the meaning of **stark** is
   a. harsh
   b. scenic
   c. exotic
   d. utterly
   e. lush

4. The author uses the second paragraph (lines 14–28) to
   a. discuss obstacles in building a dam
   b. describe the impact of the Hoover Dam
   c. build a case for water preservation
   d. explain the need for a dam
   e. extol the advances of technology

5. **Potent** (line 20) most nearly means
   a. mighty
   b. mysterious
   c. beneficial
   d. unpredictable
   e. dangerous

6. In line 20, the author uses the phrase "potent force of nature" to refer to the
   a. Hoover Dam
   b. Colorado River
   c. Boulder Canyon
   d. Grand Canyon
   e. Rocky Mountains

7. **Protrudes** (line 30) is best defined as
   a. breaks in
   b. stands
   c. juts out
   d. roars
   e. sits

8. The meaning of **placid** (line 40) is
   a. deep
   b. clear
   c. turbulent
   d. tranquil
   e. polluted

9. The benefits of the Hoover Dam project include all of the following EXCEPT the
   a. formation of a reservoir
   b. generation of electricity
   c. taming of the Colorado River
   d. development of a recreation area
   e. creation of a two-lane highway

10. **Conclusive** (line 50) most nearly means
    a. indisputable
    b. reliable
    c. debated
    d. understandable
    e. available

11. **Trenchant** (line 54) is best defined as
    a. interesting
    b. biased
    c. forceful
    d. vague
    e. inflexible

12. The author's perspective on harnessing the Colorado and other rivers is that of
    a. a concerned environmentalist
    b. a federal government official
    c. an opponent of dams
    d. an impartial reporter
    e. a proponent of dams

Two-Word Completions

Select the pair of words that best complete the meaning of each of the following passages.

1. I had hoped that the candidates would make a few _____ observations during the course of the debate. All I got, however, were the same tired old _____ that politicians have been mouthing for decades.
   a. irrelevant . . . reparations
   b. exemplary . . . pretexts
   c. trenchant . . . platitudes
   d. superficial . . . ruminations

2. High winds fanned the flames; and in no time at all, the _____ had spread to a nearby tire factory. Clouds of thick black smoke billowed up into the sky, and the _____ stench of burning rubber filled the air.
   a. contention . . . obnoxious
   b. retribution . . . indelible
   c. compunction . . . potent
   d. conflagration . . . acrid

3. After romping around with my six-year-old nephew all afternoon, I had become woefully _____. My trousers were rumpled, my shirttails were hanging out, and my tie was all _____.
   a. disheveled . . . askew
   b. disreputable . . . crestfallen
   c. garrulous . . . acrid
   d. lamentable . . . sinuous

4. During the evening, Ned must have _____ to his close acquaintance with at least a dozen celebrities. Afterward, we all agreed that his nickname, "Name-dropper Ned," was no _____.
   a. protruded . . . reparation
   b. alluded . . . misnomer
   c. misconstrued . . . pretext
   d. protruded . . . platitude

5. The trail known as "Dead Man's Curves" is so steep and _____ that even the most proficient and experienced skiers often must stop for a brief _____ before completing the course.
   a. sinuous . . . respite
   b. disreputable . . . pretext
   c. stark . . . itinerary
   d. clandestine . . . compunction

6. Utterly _____ at their upset defeat, the Belleville squad looked on dismally as the trophy they had so much _____ was awarded to their archrivals from Henderson.
   a. lamentable . . . abjured
   b. crestfallen . . . coveted
   c. disheveled . . . ruminated
   d. blithe . . . professed

7. In view of the countless crimes the dictator had committed while in power, the revolutionary tribunal expressed no _____ in seeking the sternest _____ on behalf of the people.
   a. guile . . . conflagration
   b. integrity . . . respite
   c. compunction . . . retribution
   d. pretext . . . vanguard

Idioms

In the letter to the editor regarding the lost civilizations in South America (see pages 146–147), the writer claims that the newspaper "gave short shrift" to the Moche culture. The writer means that the article gave little or no attention to the Moche people.

"Give short shrift" is an **idiom,** a common saying that expresses an action or idea in a figurative rather than literal way. Readers cannot always infer the meaning of an idiom; they often have to learn the accepted meaning and usage of each idiom.

Idioms add richness and color to spoken and written language. However, although idiomatic expressions are a natural part of everyday language, be aware of levels of formality in communication: Like slang, many idioms are informal, appropriate for casual contexts but not for use in formal situations.

Choosing the Right Idiom

Read each sentence. Use context clues to figure out the meaning of each idiom in **boldface** *print. Then write the letter of the definition for the idiom in the sentence.*

1. When Angela realized that I had been correct all along about the date for the school play, she had to **eat crow**. _____

2. I don't think you should worry about how Malik will handle his success; you know he has his **feet on the ground**. _____

3. The guard must have been **asleep at the wheel** when the thief walked right out the door with the jewels. _____

4. I had to **bite my tongue** when my sister asked me what I thought of her vintage purchase, a bulky fake fur coat in an unsettling shade of chartreuse. _____

5. I thought I understood the poem, but when the class started to talk about the theme, the discussion just **muddied the waters**. _____

6. When the lenders discovered that the business plan would cost over a million dollars, they **pulled the plug**. _____

7. Sharon roasted a turkey, mashed the potatoes, and baked a pie—**the whole nine yards**! _____

8. Growing organic tomatoes and lettuce proved to be a **cash cow** for Annie. _____

9. When our car ran out of gas, we had to **hoof it** to the nearest gas station. _____

10. My mother tried bathing our dog with lavender-scented shampoo after his encounter with a skunk, but she was just **grasping at straws**. _____

a. provided additional and confusing information

b. a profitable source of income

c. avoid saying what you really think

d. trying to accomplish something that has little chance of being successful

e. walk

f. a realistic and sensible approach to life

g. everything

h. lacking attention; not doing one's job

i. ended something; stopped giving support

j. admit a mistake or error

Writing with Idioms

Find the meaning of each idiom. (Use an online or print dictionary if necessary.) Then write a sentence for each idiom.

1. all bark and no bite

_____

2. two peas in a pod

_____

3. cut it out

_____

4. living high on the hog

_____

_____

5. all in the same boat

_____

_____

6. cross your mind

_____

_____

7. on a shoestring

_____

8. flash in the pan

_____

9. see the light

_____

10. the last straw

_____

11. keep the wolf from the door

_____

12. in a fog

_____

Denotation and Connotation

The literal meaning of a word is its **denotation**. It is the formal meaning of the word found in a dictionary. A word's denotation conveys a *neutral* tone.

Conversely, a word's **connotation** is the informal, implied meaning a reader or listener associates with it. That connotation can be either *positive* or *negative*.

Consider these synonyms for the neutral word *agree*:

> concur   consent   acquiesce   comply

Concur and *consent* have positive connotations, suggesting that an accord has been reached through mutual agreement. *Acquiesce* and *comply*, however, have negative connotations, suggesting that one side has given in to the demands of the other and that whatever agreement has been reached benefits one side more than the other.

> **Think:** Equal partners can concur with or consent to a plan of action, but a subordinate must acquiesce to or comply with a demand from a superior.

Look at these examples of words that are similar in denotation but have different connotations.

NEUTRAL	POSITIVE	NEGATIVE
grand	august	intimidating
direct	incisive	trenchant
quiet	pacify	quell

When you use a thesaurus, consider the shades of meaning that distinguish one synonym from another, and be sure you are not using a word that has inappropriately positive or negative connotations. Someone might take offense to being described as *docile* yet might be flattered to be called *placid*.

Shades of Meaning

Write a plus sign (+) in the box if the word has a positive connotation. Write a minus sign (–) if the word has a negative connotation. Put a zero (0) if the word is neutral.

1. askew ☐   **2.** blithely ☐   **3.** obnoxious ☐   **4.** lamentable ☐

5. sonorous ☐   **6.** integrity ☐   **7.** elated ☐   **8.** platitude ☐

9. disreputable ☐   **10.** protrude ☐   **11.** tacit ☐   **12.** exemplary ☐

13. potent ☐   **14.** vanguard ☐   **15.** superficial ☐   **16.** nocturnal ☐

Expressing the Connotation

Read each sentence. Select the word in parentheses that expresses the connotation (positive, negative, or neutral) given at the beginning of the sentence.

negative
1. When the trial was postponed for several months, the rancher decided to take action and seek his own (**retribution, revenge**) for the cattle theft.

negative
2. The operation was so (**clandestine, devious**) that very few officials knew about its existence.

positive
3. The dancer used (**twisting, sinuous**) movements to suggest the swaying of a tree.

positive
4. Michael was once again amazed by his young daughter's (**guile, cleverness**) as she explained how she had dealt with a problem at school.

neutral
5. The argument he gave was (**irrelevant, unrelated**) to the problem we had presented to him.

neutral
6. On a dark, cloudy day, the desert landscape can seem (**desolate, stark**) and harsh.

negative
7. For many people, the danger of talking on a cell phone while driving is a (**debatable, contentious**) matter.

positive
8. Don't you find that most grandparents are (**lenient, indulgent**) when it comes to their relationship with their grandchildren?

Challenge: Using Connotation

Choose vocabulary words from Units 10–12 to replace the highlighted words in the sentences below. Then explain how the connotation of the replacement word changes the tone of the sentence.

alluding	**coveting**	**itineraries**
compunction	**crestfallen**	**reparations**

1. Our cat shows no **hesitation** _____ in teasing our neighbors' dog by jumping onto the top of his doghouse while he is asleep inside.

_____

_____

2. The debate about issuing **reimbursements** _____ to Native Americans continues on Capitol Hill.

_____

_____

3. When news about the massive layoffs became public, the **sad** _____ expressions on the workers' faces revealed their concerns.

_____

_____

Classical Roots

dem—people; **pan**— all, every

The root *dem* appears in **endemic**, "native or confined to a particular region or people" (page 138). The root *pan* appears in **panacea**, "a remedy for all ills" (page 54). Some other words based on these roots are listed below.

demagogue	**demographics**	**demotic**	**pandemic**
pandemonium	**panoply**	**panorama**	**pantheon**

From the list of words above, choose the one that corresponds to each of the brief definitions below. Write the word in the blank space in the illustrative sentence below the definition. Use an online or print dictionary if necessary.

1. taking place over a wide area and affecting a very large number of people

Twenty-one million people died worldwide in the influenza
_____ of 1918.

2. a full suit of armor; ceremonial attire; any splendid or impressive array

Figures of knights and horses in full _____ make up one of the museum's most popular exhibits.

3. a temple or building dedicated to all the heroes or other illustrious persons; all the gods of a people

In the Greek _____, Zeus is the father of the gods.

4. statistics on human populations, such as number of people, location, migration, age, and income

The U.S. Census, which is taken every ten years, is an important source of
_____.

5. a leader who gains or holds power by appealing to the emotions or prejudices of the populace and by making false claims

_____ may cloak their true motives in the guise of patriotism.

6. relating to the common people, especially the language of the people; connected with the colloquial form of Greek spoken in modern times

Homer's epic poems *The Iliad* and *The Odyssey* are written in classical, rather than _____, Greek.

7. an unlimited view of an area in every direction; a comprehensive presentation of a subject

The _____ from the rim of the Grand Canyon is truly awe-inspiring.

8. a wild uproar, din, or commotion; literally, the dwelling place of all demons

At midnight on New Year's Eve, _____ breaks out among the revelers in Times Square.

*Read the following selection, taking note of the **boldface** words and their contexts. These words are among those you will be studying in Unit 13. As you complete the exercises in this unit, it may help to refer to the way the words are used below.*

Life on the High Seas

<Log>

This is an imaginary log of a sailor aboard the HM Bark *Endeavour* during Captain James Cook's epic 1768–1771 first voyage of discovery in the Pacific Ocean. Captain Cook visited Tahiti and charted New Zealand and the east coast of Australia. Botanists and artists on the *Endeavour* made important records of the people, flora, and fauna of each land.

5 September 1768
Nine days at sea and we are getting our sea legs. Tonight, we dined on salted beef and slabs of cheese, but I fear this is the last of our cheese ration. Ah, for an endless supply instead of what lies ahead: dried meats and—horrors!—cabbage preserved in vinegar. Still, Captain Cook has told us we must eat plenty of this dish to prevent scurvy and to set an example for the crew.

12 December 1768
Thomas, our ship's cat, is **sedate** after a busy day of ratting. His **exuberance**

for his job is an inspiration. He is always cheerful and willing and never seasick. If only that could be said of his shipmates!

21 July 1769
Endless days with no sight of land: We are **infinitesimal** specs on a vast sea. The men are restless due to the relentless and **implacable** boredom. Casks of beer and rum were damaged in last night's storm, and I fear the crew will **imbibe** the contents before long.

10 November 1769
The crew is kept busy with sail and rope repair. I heard Sam Jones grumbling that the breakfast biscuits are full of weevils and not fit to be consumed. I told him the weevils added flavor, but my **innocuous** attempt at humor fell flat.

9 January 1770
Mr. Evans, the quartermaster, is not himself. He harbors **antipathy** to all who question his navigational skills. Perhaps he has eaten bad meat?

6 April 1770
The captain has shown time and again what an **asset** he is to our king and country. Some are fearful of his **stentorian** commands that boarder on **duress**, but I say he must be forceful to keep order. We want no mutiny here!

Captain James Cook rose through the ranks, from ordinary seaman to legendary commander and explorer.

12 June 1770
Disaster! We are **beset** with troubles. Our ship ran aground on a massive reef and sustained great damage to the hull. Midshipman Munkhouse may have saved us: His idea to plug the holes has worked well as a temporary fix, and we are proceeding north in search of a harbor in which to make more thorough repairs.

3 July 1770
Weeks on land and all signs of **decorum** and discipline in the crew have vanished.

Some good news: We enjoyed tasty fish and greens for dinner—a welcome change from ship's rations. The men sang songs late into the night. As they say, better poor on land than rich at sea.

16 July 1770
Captain Cook has given us an **ultimatum**: We must complete all necessary repairs and set sail again by early August.

29 July 1770
Dined this evening with the captain; Mr. Green, the astronomer; and Mr. Banks, the botanist. Mr. Banks is excited about the many new plants he has encountered. He showed me great **compassion** when I spoke of missing my wife and children.

3 August 1770
We depart. Huzzah! Pilot whales accompanied us as we left the harbor, perhaps a good omen. We pray for good weather, calm seas, and the continued **prowess** of our brave and skilled captain to guide us to the end of our journey.

Snap the code, or go to **vocabularyworkshop.com**

The British Royal Naval vessel HM Bark Endeavour, *also known as HMS* Endeavour

Definitions

Note the spelling, pronunciation, part(s) of speech, and definition(s) of each of the following words. Then write the word in the blank spaces in the illustrative sentence(s) following. Finally, study the lists of synonyms and antonyms.

1. antipathy
(an tip' ə thē)

(*n.*) a strong dislike, hostile feeling

Sensible people normally view any form of bigotry with the most profound _____.

SYNONYMS: hostility, enmity, aversion, bad blood
ANTONYMS: attraction, appeal, allure, sympathy

2. applicable
(ap' lə kə bəl)

(*adj.*) capable of being applied; relevant, suitable

The protection against being tried for the same crime twice is not _____ in some cases.

SYNONYMS: appropriate, fit, apt, apposite
ANTONYMS: inappropriate, unsuitable, irrelevant

3. asset
(as' et)

(*n.*) something of value; a resource; an advantage

By law, an annual report must include a detailed breakdown of a company's _____ and liabilities.

SYNONYMS: property, holding, endowment
ANTONYMS: drawback, handicap, liability

4. beset
(bē set')

(*v.*) to attack from all sides; to surround, hem in; (*adj.*, *part.*) harassed, troubled; studded (as with jewels)

Every federal administration must grapple with the economic woes that _____ the nation.

The crown worn by England's monarchs is a gorgeous object _____ with fabulous precious stones.

SYNONYMS: (*v.*) assail, harass, badger, pester, torment

5. compassion
(kəm pash' ən)

(*n.*) sympathy for another's suffering; pity

Without the _____ and generosity of donors and volunteers, many charitable organizations would have to shut their doors.

SYNONYMS: concern, commiseration, empathy
ANTONYMS: indifference, callousness, heartlessness

6. decorum
(di kôr' əm)

(*n.*) proper behavior, good taste; orderliness

Legislative assemblies preserve _____ by operating under the rules of parliamentary procedure.

SYNONYMS: seemliness, good form, propriety
ANTONYMS: impropriety, bad form, bad taste

7. duress
(dū res')

(*n.*) compulsion by threat; forcible confinement

Political prisoners are sometimes subjected to a mild form of _____ called *house arrest*.

SYNONYMS: intimidation, coercion; ANTONYMS: persuasion, coaxing

8. exuberant
(eg zü' bər ənt)

(*adj.*) high-spirited, enthusiastic, unrestrained; excessive, abundant

Unable to control their _____ spirits, the fans of the popular singer cheered their idol loudly.

SYNONYMS: lively, ebullient, irrepressible, lavish
ANTONYMS: depressed, despondent, sulky, restrained

9. facsimile
(fak sim' ə lē)

(*n.*) an exact copy

A _____ of the U.S. Constitution is displayed in many social studies classrooms.

SYNONYMS: replica, duplicate, clone
ANTONYMS: variation, modification, permutation

10. imbibe
(im bīb')

(*v.*) to drink; to take in, absorb

An inquisitive person can _____ knowledge from many sources.

SYNONYMS: swallow, gulp, quaff, digest
ANTONYMS: eject, emit, expel, discharge

11. implacable
(im plak' ə bəl)

(*adj.*) not to be satisfied or pacified; unyielding

The peoples of the Arctic have shown that nature need not be an _____ foe.

SYNONYMS: relentless, inexorable, unappeasable
ANTONYMS: lenient, indulgent, permissive, flexible

12. infinitesimal
(in fin ə tes' ə məl)

(*adj.*) so small as to be almost immeasurable; minute

To a fussy housekeeper, even an _____ amount of dust on a tabletop is unacceptable.

SYNONYMS: tiny, minuscule; ANTONYMS: vast, immense, huge, infinite

13. innocuous
(i näk' yü əs)

(*adj.*) harmless, inoffensive; insignificant

Conversation at a dinner party may sometimes be confined to pleasant and _____ generalities.

SYNONYMS: feeble, impotent, unobjectionable, insipid
ANTONYMS: harmful, dangerous, pernicious, toxic, virulent

14. militate
(mil' ə tāt)

(*v.*) to have effect or force on or against someone or something, fight against

Health experts _____ strongly against a diet that is high in calories, fat, and salt.

SYNONYMS: counter, oppose, work against

15. patent
(pat′ ənt)

(*n.*) exclusive rights over an invention; copyright; (*v.*) to arrange or obtain such rights; (*adj.*) plain, open to view; copyrighted

When the _____ on a drug expires, any manufacturer may produce it.

By the time of his death in 1931, Thomas Alva Edison had _____ more inventions than any other American of his time.

During cross-examination a skilled lawyer may catch a key hostile witness in a _____ falsehood.

SYNONYMS: (*n.*) exclusive license; (*adj.*) evident
ANTONYMS: (*adj.*) concealed, hidden, secret

16. prowess
(prau′ əs)

(*n.*) distinguished bravery; superior skill or ability

The Greek hero Achilles won fame for his _____ in the Trojan War.

SYNONYMS: valor, courage, heroism, mastery, proficiency
ANTONYMS: cowardice, incompetence, ineptitude

17. sedate
(sə dāt′)

(*adj.*) quiet, settled, sober; (*v.*) to administer a tranquilizer

At concerts of classical music, audiences generally behave in a _____ and attentive manner.

A doctor may decide to _____ a patient who has suffered a severe emotional shock or physical injury.

SYNONYMS: (*adj.*) unruffled, composed, cool and collected
ANTONYMS: (*adj.*) loud, brash, flashy, flamboyant, garish, flighty

18. stentorian
(sten tôr′ ē ən)

(*adj.*) extremely loud

Some public speakers favor a _____ delivery and emphatic gestures to drive home their message to their listeners.

SYNONYMS: thundering, deafening, earsplitting
ANTONYMS: hushed, inaudible, whispered, mute

19. stipulate
(stip′ yə lāt)

(*v.*) to arrange specifically; to require as a condition of agreement

A financial institution may _____ that all its employees be fingerprinted.

SYNONYMS: specify, contract, provide for

20. ultimatum
(əl tə mā′ təm)

(*n.*) a final proposal or statement of conditions

As a strike deadline draws near, both labor and management can be expected to issue _____.

SYNONYM: final terms

Choosing the Right Word

*Select the **boldface** word that better completes each sentence. You might refer to the selection on pages 164–165 to see how most of these words are used in context.*

1. One of the many (**assets, facsimiles**) of the Globe Theater is its costumes—elaborate outfits that are made from luxuriant fabrics.

2. Some of the lessons that we learned during the Great Depression are (**implacable, applicable**) to our economic problems today.

3. My study of astronomy gave me a sense of the importance of (**infinitesimal, exuberant**) human beings and our tiny planet in a boundless universe.

4. His (**prowess, duress**) as a speaker quickly made him a leading figure in the Senate.

5. It does little good to feel (**decorum, compassion**) for those less fortunate than ourselves if we are not willing to make sacrifices to help them.

Dame Judi Dench plays Titania and Oliver Chris plays Bottom in a 2010 production of Shakespeare's *A Midsummer Night's Dream.*

6. They were so (**exuberant, innocuous**) in their praise that I soon began to suspect either their judgment or their sincerity.

7. As he watched his house go up in flames, he felt that he was the victim of an (**innocuous, implacable**) fate.

8. Without actually understanding much of what the speaker was saying, the audience seemed to (**imbibe, beset**) her optimism and vigor.

9. The politician's poor showing in the polls and the failure of her fund-raising efforts (**militated, stipulated**) against her entering the presidential race.

10. What good does it do to include all those (**stipulations, facsimiles**) in the agreement if there are no provisions for enforcing them?

11. The authorities suspected that the hostage's statement was made not voluntarily but under (**patent, duress**).

12. Mistaking the (**sedate, stentorian**) backfire of the truck for a sudden burst of gunfire, we ducked behind a parked car for safety.

13. You are in deep trouble if you combine a strong taste for high living with an equally strong (**antipathy, asset**) for hard work.

14. At my niece's birthday party, I was concerned about the enormous amounts of punch, soda, and other sugary drinks the children were (**imbibing, sedating**).

15. Unable to roar and intimidate those around him, the Cowardly Lion hoped the Great Wizard could help him exhibit his (**prowess, compassion**) as king of the beasts.

16. To show their (**decorum, exuberance**) during the play-offs, many football fans paint their faces and wear wild costumes.

17. "Here's the (**ultimatum, antipathy**)," said Father. "Pass all your courses, or forget about attending the senior prom."

18. Someone's most valuable (**prowess, asset**) may be the ability to analyze complex problems quickly and competently.

19. Although he was (**beset, imbibed**) by creditors, a tough employer, and medical problems, he never seemed to lose his zest for living.

20. In this synthetic world of ours, I sometimes wonder if my life is genuine or just a(n) (**ultimatum, facsimile**) of the real thing.

21. Her sense of (**compassion, decorum**) is so strict that she often makes other people feel stiff and uncomfortable.

22. A person's modest and (**stentorian, sedate**) appearance may mask an iron determination and a sharp temper.

23. The mistake in identification was so (**patent, infinitesimal**) that the suspect was released with the apologies of the arresting officer.

24. The tough leadership we need in this new century will not come from uncertain and (**applicable, innocuous**) personalities.

25. Did you (**stipulate, imbibe**) that you wanted the recliner, not the rocking chair?

 **Synonyms**

*Choose the word from this unit that is the same or most nearly the same in meaning as the **boldface** word or expression in the phrase. Write that word on the line. Use a dictionary if necessary.*

1. providing the **pertinent** papers for admission _____

2. a **reproduction** of a famous painting _____

3. the **obvious** stupidity of the remark _____

4. **defy** the adoption of the policy _____

5. **assimilate** the wisdom of a lifetime _____

6. **spell out** the duties to be performed _____

7. forced to sell all their **possessions** _____

8. rejected the dictator's **threat** _____

9. spoke in a **booming** voice _____

10. extorted evidence under **pressure** _____

Antonyms

*Choose the word from this unit that is most nearly opposite in meaning to the **boldface** word or expression in the phrase. Write that word on the line. Use a dictionary if necessary.*

1. provide an **original** birth certificate   _____

2. her **veiled** threats against the company   _____

3. **failed to enumerate** the conditions of the loan   _____

4. **support** the bond for a new school   _____

5. an event **unrelated to** the present situation   _____

Completing the Sentence

From the words in this unit, choose the one that best completes each of the following sentences. Write the word in the space provided.

1. How can you expect them to concern themselves with your problems when they are so _____ with troubles of their own?

2. Centuries-old ethnic _____ have more than once led to bloody conflict in the Balkans.

3. Although the artist's latest work was acclaimed by the critics, it seemed to me to be no more than a(n) _____ of a cardboard cereal box.

4. How quickly their _____ holiday mood became quiet and sober when they had to return to work on Monday morning!

5. During the long summer afternoons, we used to sit on the shaded veranda, _____ iced drinks and talking about life.

6. Her chief _____, both in business and in social life, are her keen intelligence and pleasant manner.

7. Her refusal to discuss even the possibility of a compromise convinced me that I was faced with a(n) _____ opponent.

8. If only he could match his _____ on the playing field with a high level of excellence in the classroom!

9. I am well on the road to becoming a millionaire because I have just been awarded the _____ for an automatic homework machine.

10. The reference material you have given me is interesting, but most of it is not _____ to my term paper.

11. The "monster" that frightened you so much during the hike last week was just a(n) _____ water snake.

12. The player's chronic shoulder injury _____ against his plan to extend his baseball career for another season.

13. We could hear the quarterback's _____ signals even above the roar of the crowd.

14. Dr. Albert Schweitzer had not only great scientific ability but also a deep sense of _____ for suffering humanity.

15. I enjoy his jokes, but he ought to bear in mind that there are certain standards of _____ to be observed at the graduation ceremony.

16. If the contract is framed by a good lawyer, it will _____ exactly when, where, and how payment is to be made.

17. The landlord's _____ was simple and direct: Pay the rent increase or get out.

18. I was amazed to see how a few years had transformed an unruly and mischievous child into a well-bred, _____ young adult.

19. American law prohibits police from arresting and holding suspects in any type of _____ without formally charging them.

20. He has his shortcomings, but compared with his great services to his community and nation, they seem all but _____.

Writing: Words in Action

1. Look back at "Life on the High Seas" (pages 164–165). Suppose you are Captain Cook, commander of the *Endeavour*. Write a letter to your family, describing your experiences on the voyage and assuring them that you are well. Use at least two details from the passage and three unit words.

2. *"The real voyage of discovery consists not in seeking new landscapes, but in having new eyes." —Marcel Proust*

What do you think Proust means by his statement? Do you agree or disagree with Proust's remark? Write a brief essay in which you explain the quotation and provide your opinion about Proust's statement. Support your essay with your own experience, studies, observations, and the reading (pages 164–165). Write at least three paragraphs, and use three or more words from this unit.

Vocabulary in Context

Literary Text

The following excerpts are from George Eliot's novels Silas Marner *and* The Mill on the Floss. *Some of the words you have studied in this unit appear in* **boldface** *type. Complete each statement below the excerpt by circling the letter of the correct answer.*

1. Silas now found himself and his cottage suddenly **beset** by mothers who wanted him to charm away the whooping-cough, or bring back the milk, and by men who wanted stuff against the rheumatics or the knots in the hands; and, to secure themselves against a refusal, the applicants brought silver in their palms. (*Silas Marner*)

   If a person is **beset** by something, he is
   - a. shocked
   - b. ignored
   - c. robbed
   - d. besieged

2. "Dear, dear! Master Marner," said Dolly, with gentle distress and **compassion**. "Had you never no father nor mother as taught you to say your prayers, and as there's good words and good things to keep us from harm?" (*Silas Marner*)

   Someone who shows **compassion** is NOT
   - a. kind
   - b. sympathetic
   - c. aloof
   - d. amenable

3. ...[T]he square-shouldered, clumsy, high-featured Priscilla wore a dress the **facsimile** of her pretty sister's.... (*Silas Marner*)

   If a dress is a **facsimile** it is a(n)
   - a. original
   - b. reproduction
   - c. prototype
   - d. travesty

"George Eliot" was the pen name of Mary Ann Evans, an English novelist, poet, and essayist.

4. The old Squire was an **implacable** man: he made resolutions in violent anger, and he was not to be moved from them after his anger had subsided—as fiery volcanic matters cool and harden into rock. (*Silas Marner*)

   A person who is **implacable** is
   - a. negligent
   - b. harmless
   - c. obstinate
   - d. indecisive

5. He paused a little to consider how he should pray about Euclid—whether he should ask to see what it meant, or whether there was any other mental state which would be more **applicable** to the case. (*The Mill on the Floss*)

   Something that is **applicable** is
   - a. pertinent
   - b. unrelated
   - c. trivial
   - d. tedious

Interactive Quiz

Snap the code, or go to **vocabularyworkshop.com**

*Read the following selection, taking note of the **boldface** words and their contexts. These words are among those you will be studying in Unit 14. As you complete the exercises in this unit, it may help to refer to the way the words are used below.*

A Short History of Hygiene

<Informational Essay>

Hygeia, goddess of health and cleanliness

Cleanliness has deep roots in human civilization. The word *hygiene* is derived from the name of an ancient Greek goddess. Hygeia, the goddess of health and cleanliness, was said to prevent disease, and when an epidemic threatened, the Greeks went with **alacrity** to her temples. Ancient Romans worshipped Hygeia too, and Rome was famous for its advanced hygienic standards. Historians **laud** the Romans for both building aqueducts that carried fresh water into Rome and public toilets that collected waste. Dotting the city were comfortable bathhouses, where people would gather to **loll** in the waters. Perhaps it was here that Romans first earned their reputation as a **loquacious** people, for they would

The ruins of a thermal bath in Italy

pass idle time chatting with friends. An unexpected invader, however, added a **dissonant** note to Rome's hygienic way of life: Head lice were common, and without soap, these parasites were hard to control. To **alleviate** this problem, Romans covered their bodies with oil and then scraped themselves clean with an instrument called a *strigil*. Unfortunately, the Romans' hygienic way of life was endangered when barbarians sacked Rome in the fourth century AD. These **bellicose** invaders were not **magnanimous** to their enemies; they destroyed as much of the Roman civilization as possible. **Appalled** by the destruction, Romans fled for their lives, and the highly ordered Roman Empire soon collapsed.

Subsequent centuries in Europe were, hygienically speaking, the **antithesis** of what is prevalent today. The time between AD 500 and AD 1500, **disparaged** as the Dark Ages, was a period when the average life expectancy barely reached into the mid-thirties. Advice about hygiene in the Dark Ages seems almost **droll** today: A Latin proverb from the time warns people that "frequent bathing causes a wasting body." Certainly, sanitation and clean water were lacking in large cities, lice infestation was a constant problem, and diseases spread quickly. The Crusaders, soldiers in Holy Wars, brought soap back from the East, but it was a luxury and not widely used. Authorities issued **edicts** against public bathhouses, fearing their use led to immorality, and many years passed before these orders were **rescinded**. In colder climates, bathing was infrequent because of the lack of heating. Also, in an era of plagues—which killed over a third of Europe's population—many people believed the skin absorbed diseases from water. In the absence of scientific knowledge and with the cause of the terrifying plagues unexplained, people accepted such misinformation. While a full bath would have been an infrequent indulgence, most people did wash their hands and face with some regularity.

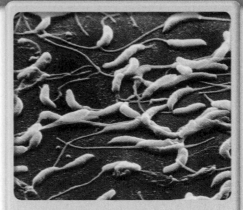

Commonly found in fresh water, these bacteria would have alarmed Medievals.

The discovery that bacteria caused disease, a revelation that came in the mid-nineteenth century, brought about a sea change in hygiene and public health. To control germs, experts said it was **mandatory** to wash hands regularly. In addition, to avoid disease, sewage had to be disposed of safely, and water had to be pure. Meeting these goals, a challenging undertaking, continues to this day. In the quest for better hygiene, science and technology **elucidated** the importance of new and better ways to promote health. Even relatively simple inventions, like the flush toilet and chlorinated water, have probably saved millions of lives. Washing machines and detergents played a big role too—they helped people clean clothes quickly and thoroughly. In the struggle to prevent bacterial diseases, modern society has clearly gone the extra mile. Hygeia would be pleased, for although she is no longer worshipped as a goddess, people today are cleaner than ever.

Snap the code, or go to **vocabularyworkshop.com**

Definitions

Note the spelling, pronunciation, part(s) of speech, and definition(s) of each of the following words. Then write the word in the blank spaces in the illustrative sentence(s) following. Finally, study the lists of synonyms and antonyms.

1. alacrity
(ə lak′ rə tē)

(n.) a cheerful readiness; brisk and eager action

Neighbors responded with _____ to the woman's cries for help.

SYNONYMS: promptness, willingness, celerity
ANTONYMS: reluctance, unwillingness, hesitancy

2. alleviate
(ə lē′ vē āt)

(v.) to relieve, make more bearable

The doctors and nurses did everything they could to _____ the patient's severe pain.

SYNONYMS: lessen, allay, mitigate, assuage

3. antithesis
(an tith′ ə sis)

(n.) the direct opposite, a sharp contrast

Discriminatory practices may be said to constitute the very _____ of our nation's democratic ideals.

SYNONYMS: contrary, antipode

4. appall
(ə pôl′)

(v.) to fill with dismay or horror

The assassination of President John F. Kennedy in 1963 _____ the nation and the world.

SYNONYMS: shock, stupefy, horrify
ANTONYMS: please, cheer, gladden, elate, exhilarate

5. bellicose
(bel′ i kōs)

(adj.) warlike in manner or temperament; quarrelsome

Teddy Roosevelt's foreign policy was often driven by a rather _____ brand of patriotism.

SYNONYMS: aggressive, combative, belligerent
ANTONYMS: amicable, peaceable, pacific

6. disparage
(dis pâr′ ij)

(v.) to belittle, speak slightingly of; to undervalue

Don't you think voters are getting awfully tired of listening to politicians _____ their opponents' voting records?

SYNONYMS: degrade, decry, run down, underrate
ANTONYMS: praise, extol, laud, plug

7. dissonant
(dis′ ə nənt)

(adj.) not in harmony; disagreeing, at odds

The clamor of _____ voices could be heard clearly through the closed doors of the meeting room.

SYNONYMS: grating, unmelodious, irreconcilable
ANTONYMS: harmonious, agreeing, euphonious

8. droll
(drōl)

(*adj.*) amusingly odd

The hero or heroine of a popular sitcom may be surrounded by a cast of _____ eccentrics.

SYNONYMS: comical, humorous, whimsical, zany
ANTONYMS: humorless, solemn, dour

9. edict
(ē′ dikt)

(*n.*) an order issued by someone in authority

Only in fairy tales can human unhappiness and misery be banished forever by royal _____.

SYNONYMS: command, decree, proclamation

10. elucidate
(i lü′ sə dāt)

(*v.*) to clarify, explain

The precise meaning of a passage in *Middlemarch* is sometimes hard to _____.

SYNONYMS: interpret, expound, explicate
ANTONYMS: obscure, becloud, muddy, obfuscate

11. laud
(lôd)

(*v.*) to praise

At the assembly the principal _____ both students and teachers for the schoolwide improvement in reading scores.

SYNONYMS: hail, extol, glorify, exalt
ANTONYMS: criticize, censure, belittle, disparage

12. loll
(läl)

(*v.*) to act in a lazy manner; to lounge; to recline, droop

There is nothing I would rather do on a hot, humid summer afternoon than _____ in a hammock under a tree.

SYNONYMS: loaf, loiter, sag, dangle

13. loquacious
(lō kwā′ shəs)

(*adj.*) talkative, wordy; fond of talking

My dinner companion was so _____ that our conversation quickly turned into a monologue.

SYNONYMS: gossipy, voluble, garrulous, long-winded
ANTONYMS: silent, reticent, closemouthed, terse, taciturn

14. magnanimous
(mag nan′ ə məs)

(*adj.*) generous in forgiving, above small meanness

The general's victory was so decisive that he could afford to be _____ toward his former enemies.

SYNONYMS: unselfish, charitable, noble, bighearted
ANTONYMS: petty, selfish, unforgiving, spiteful

15. mandatory
(man′ də tôr ē)

(*adj.*) required, obligatory

A union contract may stipulate that members are to receive a _____ annual cost-of-living increase.

SYNONYMS: compulsory, requisite, imperative
ANTONYMS: optional, voluntary, discretionary

16. nondescript
(nän də skript′)

(*adj.*) ordinary, not outstanding; not easily classified

Fashion critics judged the designer's fall clothing line to be disappointingly _____.

SYNONYMS: plain, unremarkable, unimpressive
ANTONYMS: remarkable, vivid, prepossessing

17. phlegmatic
(fleg mat′ ik)

(*adj.*) slow-moving, sluggish; unemotional

Sloths are such _____ creatures that they have earned the reputation of being the slowest animals on Earth.

SYNONYMS: lethargic, indolent, torpid, impassive
ANTONYMS: emotional, sensitive, thin-skinned, excitable

18. rescind
(ri sind′)

(*v.*) to repeal, cancel

A sitting Congress sometimes _____ statutes passed by its predecessors.

SYNONYMS: withdraw, retract, annul, abrogate
ANTONYMS: affirm, endorse, uphold, ratify

19. vivacious
(və vā′ shəs)

(*adj.*) lively, sprightly, full of energy

A _____ individual will certainly never lack for companions.

SYNONYMS: spirited, animated, ebullient
ANTONYMS: dull, spiritless, listless, indolent

20. whet
(whet)

(*v.*) to sharpen, put an edge on; to make keen or eager

In most mystery novels, the first chapter is designed to _____ your curiosity to find out "who done it."

SYNONYMS: hone, excite, stimulate
ANTONYMS: blunt, deaden, stifle, dampen

Choosing the Right Word

*Select the **boldface** word that better completes each sentence. You might refer to the selection on pages 174–175 to see how most of these words are used in context.*

Mahatma Gandhi spread the philosophy of *satyagraha*, or nonviolent civil resistance to government tyranny.

1. In the eyes of such leaders as Gandhi and Martin Luther King, Jr., violence is the very (**edict, antithesis**) of a civilized society.

2. Only a truly (**phlegmatic, vivacious**) person could have remained calm in the face of such provocation.

3. The cake was delicious, but the serving was so small that it did little more than (**elucidate, whet**) my appetite.

4. In the fight against air pollution, many states have made filtering devices (**droll, mandatory**) for all cars sold within their borders.

5. Observers doubted that any coalition composed of such (**magnanimous, dissonant**) factions could long refrain from petty infighting.

6. It is sometimes said that women are more (**loquacious, bellicose**) than men, but all the men I know do their full share of talking.

7. Churchill told the British to be resolute in war, defiant in defeat, and (**magnanimous, loquacious**) in victory.

8. The only truly effective way to (**appall, alleviate**) the poverty of developing nations is to help increase their capacity to produce wealth.

9. An (**edict, antithesis**) was issued by the Holy Roman Emperor to ban the writings of Martin Luther because he challenged the absolute authority of the pope.

10. By (**rescinding, elucidating**) the concept of a pyramid scheme in her opening statement, the attorney hoped to clarify why her client was innocent.

11. Her manner of speaking is so (**vivacious, phlegmatic**) that even her most commonplace remarks seem to suggest charm and excitement.

12. There must be a serious flaw in the character of those who have a constant need to (**laud, disparage**) others.

13. This young man has been (**lauded, lolled**) by many colleagues and fans as the most creative game designer in the industry.

14. Although Americans are not a (**bellicose, mandatory**) people, they have proven themselves prepared to defend their nation at any cost.

15. His jokes were actually not too good, but his (**nondescript, droll**) manner of delivering them made a big hit with the audience.

16. The houses in that development are a mixture of (**dissonant, nondescript**) styles, with no particular architectural character or distinguishing features.

17. I see no reason to (**laud, disparage**) him in such glowing terms for doing no more than his duty.

18. Your relaxed and lackadaisical attitude reveals a (**phlegmatic, loquacious**) personality, which means that you would not be happy in a fast-moving, high-pressure job.

19. Reporters asked the mayor to (**elucidate, alleviate**) her ambiguous remarks about her plans to seek higher office.

20. Maya pretended to be indifferent about going to the dance, but I noticed that she accepted Joshua's invitation with (**antithesis, alacrity**).

21. What (**appalled, lolled**) us even more than their fearful living conditions was that the refugees seemed to have lost all hope.

22. The expression, "What goes up must come down," might be termed an (**alacrity, edict**) of nature.

23. Would you rather (**rescind, loll**) in the back seat of a chauffeured limousine or drive your own convertible?

24. Because of the incidents that occurred during hazing week, the school may (**whet, rescind**) the rules that allow fraternity initiations.

25. Do you have any remedies that can (**disparage, alleviate**) an upset stomach?

 **Synonyms**   *Choose the word from this unit that is the same or most nearly the same in meaning as the **boldface** word or expression in the phrase. Write that word on the line. Use a dictionary if necessary.*

1. joined the **dynamic** group of dancers   _____

2. refused to obey the **directive**   _____

3. agreed to the proposal with **dispatch**   _____

4. **illuminate** fine points of the law   _____

5. a preview that **arouses** your curiosity   _____

6. a series of **strident** chords   _____

7. **lighten** the tax burden   _____

8. known to have a **stolid** temperament   _____

9. **revoke** the ban on parking in midtown   _____

10. a truly **commonplace** personality   _____

Antonyms

*Choose the word from this unit that is most nearly opposite in meaning to the **boldface** word or expression in the phrase. Write that word on the line. Use a dictionary if necessary.*

1. conveys a **lively** personality   _____

2. **dulls** the blade of an axe   _____

3. adopted a **conciliatory** attitude   _____

4. enjoys a **languid** Sunday afternoon   _____

5. purchased the most **distinctive** car on the lot   _____

Completing the Sentence

From the words in this unit, choose the one that best completes each of the following sentences. Write the word in the space provided.

1. Instead of waiting for government help, let's do all we can right now to _____ the sufferings of the flood victims.

2. His disposition is so _____ that he is apt to turn a simple difference of opinion into a full-scale donnybrook.

3. In spite of her inexperience as a programmer, she attacked her new job with _____ and made good progress.

4. Although in America voting is not _____, every qualified citizen has a duty to go to the polls in every election.

5. Unlike you, I have never lived in France, but is that any reason for you to _____ my efforts to speak French?

6. The principal finally _____ the unfair school regulation that prevented new students from trying out for the varsity teams.

7. You can make requests and suggestions if you wish, but please don't issue any _____.

8. When the speaker tried to _____ the statement he had just made, I became more confused than ever.

9. In a time of fast-talking, loud comedians, is there a place for his kind of quiet, _____ humor?

10. At that dull, stodgy party, her _____ personality was like a breath of fresh air.

11. His enthusiastic and colorful description of the new series on public TV has _____ my desire to see it.

12. I shall never forget your _____ offer to coach me, even though we were competing for the same role in the play.

13. Is this _____ little house the "magnificent mansion" that you've been telling us about all these weeks?

14. Their sarcastic remarks introduced a(n) _____ note into what had been a harmonious meeting.

15. Even the state troopers, who had been hardened by long experience, were _____ when they came on the scene of the automobile accident.

16. He may appear to be _____, but his friends are aware of the strong emotions simmering beneath his quiet exterior.

17. I'm usually quite energetic, but there are times when I want to do nothing but _____ about and listen to my favorite music.

18. I would have preferred to enjoy the paintings quietly, without listening to the explanations of the _____ guide.

19. His idle, pleasure-seeking way of life is the exact _____ of all that his hardworking parents had expected of him.

20. Though her friends _____ her many achievements, her enemies ridiculed them.

Writing: Words in Action

1. Look back at "A Short History of Hygiene" (pages 174–175). Suppose you were given the opportunity to enlighten the people of the so-called Dark Ages about the importance of cleanliness. To convince them that good hygiene is essential to healthy living, write a public service announcement explaining why all citizens should wash regularly. Use at least two details from the passage and three unit words.

2. New discoveries and expanded knowledge often prompt changes in the way people live. What new discoveries, improved information, or revised ideas in recent years have prompted—or may later prompt—changes in lifestyle? Write a brief essay in which you describe a change that is now taking place (or may soon take place) as the result of a new discovery or improved information. Support your ideas with your own experience, observations, studies, and the reading (pages 174–175). Write at least three paragraphs, and use three or more words from this unit.

Vocabulary in Context

Literary Text

The following excerpts are from **The House of the Seven Gables** *by Nathaniel Hawthorne. Some of the words you have studied in this unit appear in* **boldface** *type. Complete each statement below the excerpt by circling the letter of the correct answer.*

1. With miles and miles of varied scenery between, there was no scene for her save the seven old gable-peaks.... This one old house was everywhere! It transported its great, lumbering bulk with more than railroad speed, and set itself **phlegmatically** down on whatever spot she glanced at.

   To position something **phlegmatically** assumes an attitude of

   a. urgency
   b. superiority
   c. indifference
   d. caring

2. His present phase, as a daguerreotypist, was of no more importance in his own view, nor likely to be more permanent, than any of the preceding ones. It had been taken up with the careless **alacrity** of an adventurer, who had his bread to earn. It would be thrown aside as carelessly....

   A person who exhibits **alacrity** is NOT

   a. sluggish
   b. quick
   c. decisive
   d. spirited

Nathaniel Hawthorne, nineteenth-century novelist and short-story writer

3. Then she was attracted by a chaise rapidly passing, and watched its moist and glistening top, and its splashing wheels, until it had turned the corner, and refused to carry any further her idly trifling, because **appalled** and overburdened, mind.

   A mind that is **appalled** is

   a. closed off
   b. idle
   c. judgmental
   d. dismayed

4. Indeed they have; and the hour is noted on a card, which is, or ought to be, in Judge Pyncheon's right vest-pocket. Let him go thither, and **loll** at ease upon his moneybags! He has lounged long enough in the old chair!

   To **loll** means

   a. to look upon
   b. to lie around
   c. to laugh merrily
   d. to run through

5. The chicken, hereupon, though almost as venerable in appearance as its mother...mustered **vivacity** enough to flutter upward and alight on Phoebe's shoulder.

   An animal that exhibits **vivacity** is

   a. indecisive
   b. lethargic
   c. clever
   d. vigorous

Interactive Quiz

Snap the code, or go to **vocabularyworkshop.com**

*Read the following selection, taking note of the **boldface** words and their contexts. These words are among those you will be studying in Unit 15. As you complete the exercises in this unit, it may help to refer to the way the words are used below.*

World-Famous Dance Troupe Announces First U.S. Tour

<Press Release>

FOR IMMEDIATE RELEASE:

U.S. Tour of Ballets Russes to Launch in New York City

New York, January 3—

The Metropolitan Civic Association is proud to announce its exclusive sponsorship of the first American tour of the celebrated Ballets Russes. The world's most prestigious dance company will kick off its sixteen-city tour of the United States with a performance in New York City. Tickets to opening night will be available at the M.C.A. box office beginning Monday.

The Ballets Russes has enjoyed great success—and provoked considerable controversy—since its inaugural performance seven years ago in Paris. Unique among dance troupes, the Ballets Russes ensures its every production is an artistic collaboration with some of the most notable composers, choreographers, costumers, and set designers of our day. Onstage, its accomplished troupe of thirteen dancers is led by the great Vaslav Nijinsky, rightly hailed as the finest male dancer of his generation.

The company was established in 1909 by the Russian impresario Sergei Diaghilev, whose **zealous** support of modern dance boldly thrust classical dance traditions into the twentieth century.

Sergei Diaghilev

Igor Stravinsky

His avant-garde productions offended some early audience members, who were **voluble** in their resistance to the Ballets Russes's break with classical ballet. Most spectators were **receptive** to Diaghilev's ideas, however, and critics now **concur** that any Ballets Russes performance is the epitome of Modernism.

Critical to the company's success has been the music of Russian composer Igor Stravinsky. His contributions to the Ballets Russes have not been without controversy, however. No one familiar with the recent history of this outstanding dance troupe will fail to recall reports of the 1913 **fracas** in Paris, when the composer's *The Rite of Spring* provoked the opening-night audience to near **pandemonium**. An unfamiliar sound on the dance stage, Stravinsky's adventurous music was considered too **abrasive** an accompaniment to ballet. Disparaged as **grotesque**, the Ballets Russes dancers' movements, too, came under fire. Yet lovers of ballet on both sides of the Atlantic have rapidly **acclimated** themselves to change, and by uniting modern movement with modern music, the Ballets Russes has brought a fresh perspective to dance.

A performance of *The Firebird*, Stravinsky's first popular sensation for the Ballets Russes, will inaugurate the American tour. The composer's *Petrushka*

Nijinsky and corps in "L'Apres-midi d'un faune"

will be included in the performance schedule as well. Stravinsky created this work for Nijinsky. The fanciful plot tells the story of Petrushka, a puppet made of straw who comes to life. A love triangle reaches its climax when Petrushka is slain by his rival. However, the hero then returns to life as a ghost and visits the enemies who have **repressed** him.

The great Nijinsky himself is rumored to be joining the tour later this season. Monsieur Diaghilev, always **reticent**, has refused to comment on the possibility of a performance by Nijinksy in the role of *Petrushka* while the troupe is on these shores. It is therefore with sincere appreciation and high hopes that the M.C.A. commends the Ballets Russes to our friends and supporters.

Tickets to the New York City performances, which begin at the Metropolitan Opera House on January 17, will doubtless be at a premium. So we entreat art lovers not to suffer the **chagrin** of being turned away at the door! Do not **renounce** this rare opportunity to witness one of the most dazzling spectacles of this or any era. No more **vehement** advocate for modern art can be found

than Monsieur Diaghilev. Just as a master chef selects choice ingredients and blends them to create a **savory** meal, Monsieur Diaghilev possesses an uncanny talent to fuse music and dance, whimsy and spectacle. His every production has stirred hitherto **complacent** audiences everywhere the troupe has performed. We have every reason to believe that each U.S. performance by the Ballets Russes will be met with **raucous** applause.

For tickets to the New York performances, please contact the Metropolitan Civic Association at 51 West 11th Street, or telephone Mr. Constantine Z. Schelling or Mrs. Amelie Ziolkowski at REgent 4-2636.

Snap the code, or go to
vocabularyworkshop.com

Definitions

Note the spelling, pronunciation, part(s) of speech, and definition(s) of each of the following words. Then write the word in the blank spaces in the illustrative sentence(s) following. Finally, study the lists of synonyms and antonyms.

1. abrasive
(ə brā′ siv)

(*adj.*) causing irritation, harsh; grinding or wearing down;
(*n.*) a substance used to smooth or polish

Within every family there are some relationships that tend to be _____.

Pumice, a natural _____, is a highly porous type of glass that is produced by volcanic eruptions.

SYNONYMS: (*adj.*) chafing, grating, rasping, erosive
ANTONYMS: (*adj.*) smooth, polished, satiny, oily

2. acclimate
(ak′ lə māt)

(*v.*) to adapt to a new climate, environment, or situation

You may find it difficult to _____ to a new school if you arrive in the middle of the year.

SYNONYMS: accustom, learn the ropes

3. chagrin
(shə grin′)

(*n.*) irritation or humiliation caused by disappointment or frustration; (*v.*) to cause such a feeling

Much to my _____, I placed a mere fourth in the 100-meter freestyle.

The lukewarm reception accorded his first and only opera, *Fidelio*, deeply _____ the composer Ludwig van Beethoven.

SYNONYMS: (*n.*) vexation, mortification; (*v.*) abash, mortify
ANTONYMS: (*n.*) jubilation, exultation, triumph; (*v.*) exult, delight

4. complacent
(kəm plā′ sənt)

(*adj.*) self-satisfied; overly content

_____ individuals are, by definition, overly pleased with their lot in life.

SYNONYMS: smug, unconcerned
ANTONYM: discontented

5. concur
(kən kər′)

(*v.*) to express agreement, approve

It is indeed rare for eyewitness accounts of an accident to _____ in every detail.

SYNONYMS: agree, assent, ratify, sanction
ANTONYMS: disagree, differ, part company

6. defamation
(def ə mā′ shən)

(*n.*) slander or libel

Celebrities sometimes find that they have no choice but to sue tabloids for _____.

SYNONYMS: vilification, calumny; ANTONYMS: salute, tribute

7. explicate
(eks′ plə kāt)

(*v.*) to make plain or clear, explain; to interpret

The students listened attentively as the math teacher
_____ the geometry theorem.

SYNONYMS: elucidate, untangle, spell out
ANTONYMS: confuse, bewilder, obscure, obfuscate

8. fracas
(frā′ kəs)

(*n.*) a noisy quarrel or brawl

Do you think that the _____ on some talk
shows are spontaneous or staged?

SYNONYMS: row, altercation, rhubarb, brouhaha
ANTONYMS: agreement, accord, unanimity, harmony

9. grotesque
(grō tesk′)

(*adj.*) unnatural, distorted; bizarre

Gargoyles, the _____ beasts carved on
many Gothic churches, are actually drainage spouts.

SYNONYMS: fantastic, outlandish, ugly, deformed
ANTONYMS: appealing, attractive, comely

10. pandemonium
(pan də mō′ nē əm)

(*n.*) a wild uproar, din, or commotion

The whirl of activity on the floor of a stock exchange often
looks and sounds like utter _____.

SYNONYMS: chaos, bedlam, three-ring circus
ANTONYMS: order, calm, tranquillity, peace, repose

11. raucous
(rô′ kəs)

(*adj.*) disagreeably harsh-sounding; disorderly

A _____ voice can be a liability for
someone wishing to pursue a career in television journalism.

SYNONYMS: boisterous, clamorous, strident
ANTONYMS: placid, tranquil, peaceful, serene, pastoral

12. receptive
(ri sep′ tiv)

(*adj.*) open and responsive to ideas or suggestions

People will generally be _____ to criticism
of their work if it is given in a constructive manner.

SYNONYMS: open-minded, tolerant, amenable
ANTONYMS: narrow-minded, intolerant, hidebound

13. renounce
(ri naúns′)

(*v.*) to give up or resign something

Throughout history, martyrs have willingly given up their lives
rather than _____ their cause.

SYNONYMS: repudiate, disown, abdicate
ANTONYMS: retain, secure, affirm, assent, aver

14. repress
(ri pres′)

(*v.*) to hold back; to put down or check by force

As history has repeatedly proved, even the most brutal tyrants cannot forever _____ the human desire for freedom.

SYNONYMS: subdue, curb, stifle, bottle up
ANTONYMS: liberate, set loose, provoke, excite

15. reticent
(ret′ ə sənt)

(*adj.*) not inclined to speak; reserved; reluctant

She is understandably _____ about discussing her most deeply held beliefs with a group of total strangers.

SYNONYMS: taciturn, closemouthed, tight-lipped
ANTONYMS: talkative, garrulous, voluble, long-winded

16. savory
(sāv′ ə rē)

(*adj.*) tasty, appetizing; pungent or salty, not sweet; inoffensive, respectable

Some of the characters a reader meets in a detective story are none too _____.

SYNONYMS: delectable, flavorful, aromatic, piquant
ANTONYMS: distasteful, unpalatable, malodorous, bland

17. somnolent
(säm′ nə lənt)

(*adj.*) sleepy, drowsy; inducing sleep

By the end of an enormous Thanksgiving feast, most diners usually feel quite _____.

SYNONYMS: groggy, soporific
ANTONYMS: alert, lively, wide-awake, stimulating

18. vehement
(vē′ ə mənt)

(*adj.*) intense, forceful, powerful

The defendant's _____ protestations of innocence failed to convince the jurors.

SYNONYMS: emphatic, vigorous, impassioned
ANTONYMS: apathetic, lukewarm, subdued, muted

19. voluble
(väl′ yə bəl)

(*adj.*) characterized by a ready flow of words; glib, fluent

Reporters never give much credence to tips that they receive from _____ but unreliable informants, however persistent.

SYNONYMS: loquacious, garrulous, long-winded, prolix
ANTONYMS: uncommunicative, reticent, terse

20. zealous
(zel′ əs)

(*adj.*) eager, earnest, devoted

Most members of my family are _____ supporters of our local high school's basketball, baseball, and football teams.

SYNONYMS: ardent, fervent, devout, dogged, gung ho
ANTONYMS: reluctant, unwilling, averse, tepid

Choosing the Right Word

*Select the **boldface** word that better completes each sentence. You might refer to the selection on pages 184–185 to see how most of these words are used in context.*

Seventeenth-century writer John Milton, author of *Paradise Lost*, stands with Shakespeare as one of the greatest English writers.

1. For centuries scholars have argued over how to (**explicate, renounce**) certain cryptic passages in Milton's plays and poems.

2. A (**fracas, chagrin**) between rival groups on the floor of the convention was swiftly quelled by security guards.

3. Some people seem to relish every (**somnolent, savory**) morsel of gossip that comes their way.

4. The workers were (**vehement, reticent**) to speak about the bank robbery, frightened that the thieves might later seek retaliation.

5. With deep (**chagrin, pandemonium**), I must confess that I was the one who neglected to hire the orchestra for the class dance.

6. We all have impulses to violence, but we must learn to (**repress, concur**) them if we are to live in a civilized society.

7. Although some people would disagree, many more would (**concur, renounce**) that the Beatles were the most influential rock band of all time.

8. Mr. Sanderson is usually a man of very few words, but he was certainly (**abrasive, voluble**) when we asked him about his operation.

9. It's not surprising that after so many years of military service, he has found it difficult to become (**acclimated, vehement**) to civilian life.

10. I was startled not so much by your disapproval of my proposal as by the (**fracas, vehemence**) with which you denounced it.

11. Some politicians are more (**zealous, voluble**) in promoting their own careers than in seeking to help the people who elected them.

12. The figures in the surrealistic painting had the (**grotesque, reticent**) appearance of characters in a nightmare.

13. After spending a month in the country, we found the sounds of rush-hour traffic in the big city more (**raucous, grotesque**) than ever.

14. Kim attributed her failure to get the lead role in the play to the director's poor judgment and remained (**raucous, complacent**) about her acting abilities.

15. Will I ever again sleep as deeply as I did on those deliciously (**raucous, somnolent**) afternoons on that hot, quiet beach?

16. Economists have spent years attempting to (**acclimate, explicate**) the causes of the 1929 stock market collapse and the years of economic depression that followed it.

17. He has a good deal of ability, but his (**zealous, abrasive**) personality has prevented him from getting ahead in the business world.

18. After a lot of persuading, our parents (**repressed, concurred**) with our plan to make a bicycle tour of New England.

19. The (**voluble, complacent**) expression on the antique doll's porcelain face seemed to proclaim, "All's right with the world."

20. In unforgettable words, the soothsayer called on mankind to (**acclimate, renounce**) the use of armed force.

21. Why is it that some people are so talkative about most things but so (**complacent, reticent**) about their own personal backgrounds?

22. Lacking a positive program of his own, he hoped to gain the support of the voters by (**explicating, defaming**) the other candidates.

23. (**Pandemonium, Defamation**) erupted when the nervous theater manager announced to the waiting crowd that the rock concert was canceled.

24. Gloria's kind words put me in such a (**receptive, savory**) frame of mind that I agreed to work on the committee before I knew what I was doing.

25. Rosemary is preferred in this soup due to its (**savory, voluble**) qualities.

Synonyms

*Choose the word from this unit that is the same or most nearly the same in meaning as the **boldface** word or expression in the phrase. Write that word on the line. Use a dictionary if necessary.*

1. need to **clarify** some of the technical language _____

2. **embarrassment** over their crushing defeat _____

3. a campaign of **mudslinging** _____

4. tried to break up the **melee** _____

5. willingly **rejected** worldly things _____

6. twisted into **monstrous** shapes _____

7. led to **tumult** on the Senate floor _____

8. made from rich and **delicious** sauces _____

9. a **fierce** debate on a controversial issue _____

10. **heavy-eyed** from studying all night _____

Antonyms

*Choose the word from this unit that is most nearly opposite in meaning to the **boldface** word or expression in the phrase. Write that word on the line. Use a dictionary if necessary.*

1. **taciturn** traveling companions   _____

2. a **motivating** environment   _____

3. an extremely **pleasant** manner   _____

4. **conceal** your intentions for the purchase   _____

5. an article outlining his **praise**   _____

Completing the Sentence

From the words in this unit, choose the one that best completes each of the following sentences. Write the word in the space provided.

1. Although I am afraid of the dentist, I must _____ my fears and go for treatment.

2. Since hockey players often crash into each other at high speed, it's not surprising that occasionally a(n) _____ develops.

3. I have great respect for your knowledge of our government, but I really cannot _____ with your opinion about the role of the judiciary.

4. The carpenter used a(n) _____ to remove the old finish from the top of the desk before revarnishing it.

5. The library became a scene of _____ when a practical joker released a number of mice.

6. When we reached Mexico City, which is over 7,000 feet above sea level, we found it difficult at first to _____ ourselves to the thinner air.

7. The answers that the candidate gave at the press conference were rambling and _____ but contained practically no hard information.

8. An accountant tried to _____ the new tax legislation to me, but when she had finished, I felt I was even more in the dark than before.

9. Both sons agreed to _____ their claims to their father's estate in favor of their widowed mother.

10. The editorial on city government was so unfair and biased that it amounted to _____ of all the elected officials of this community.

11. You can well imagine my _____ at losing such an important election by so few votes.

12. I was confident that after Dad had eaten a good meal, he would be more _____ to my request for the use of the car.

13. The conceited actor was anything but _____ in discussing his innumerable triumphs on the stage, screen, and TV.

14. _____ shouts and boos from the stands will have no effect on a good umpire's decisions.

15. We didn't expect such _____ dislike of country-and-western music from a native of Nashville.

16. For their art project the children made _____ masks that they planned to use in a play based on some myths they had read.

17. A free people cannot afford to grow _____ but must remain ever vigilant in safeguarding their liberties.

18. In an amazingly short time and with only the simplest ingredients, I had a(n) _____ stew simmering on the stove.

19. She tried hard to remain awake, but the _____ atmosphere of the warm and cozy parlor was too much for her.

20. He was just an average player when he first joined the team, but everyone admired his _____ efforts to improve his game.

Writing: Words in Action

1. Look back at "World-Famous Dance Troupe Announces First U.S. Tour," the press release for the Ballets Russes (pages 184–185). Suppose you attended a performance of the Ballets Russes. In an effort to persuade others to attend a performance by this troupe, write a review, explaining why you recommend the ballet. Use at least two details from the passage and three unit words.

2. *"To send light into the darkness of men's hearts—such is the duty of the artist."*
   —Robert Schumann

   Think about the quotation by nineteenth-century German composer Robert Schumann. Do you agree or disagree with his assessment of "the duty of the artist"? What do you think is the role of the artist—and the arts—in contemporary life? Write a brief essay in which you support your opinion with specific examples, observations, studies, and the reading (pages 184–185). Write at least three paragraphs, and use three or more words from this unit.

Vocabulary in Context

Literary Text

The following excerpts are from **Emma** by Jane Austen. Some of the words you have studied in this unit appear in **boldface** type. Complete each statement below the excerpt by circling the letter of the correct answer.

1. In short, she sat, during the first visit, looking at Jane Fairfax with twofold **complacency**; the sense of pleasure and the sense of rendering justice, and was determining that she would dislike her no longer.

   To look upon someone with **complacency** assumes
   a. gratification
   b. sorrowfulness
   c. annoyance
   d. embarrassment

2. He agreed to it, but with so quiet a "Yes," as inclined her almost to doubt his real **concurrence**; and yet there must be a very distinct sort of elegance for the fashionable world, if Jane Fairfax could be thought only ordinarily gifted with it.

   A **concurrence** is a(n)
   a. dispute
   b. emotion
   c. hesitation
   d. consent

3. How very few of those men in a rank of life to address Emma would have **renounced** their own home for Hartfield!

   When something is **renounced**, it is
   a. forsaken
   b. declared
   c. sustained
   d. honored

Kate Beckinsale and Mark Strong in *Emma*, 1996

4. ...Harriet had acknowledged her admiration and preference of Frank Churchill before she had ever given her a hint on the subject; but she felt completely guilty of having encouraged what she might have **repressed**.

   When a feeling is **repressed**, it is
   a. exposed
   b. accepted
   c. constrained
   d. suspected

5. ...Miss Bates soon came—"Very happy and obliged"—but Emma's conscience told her that there was not the same cheerful **volubility** as before—less ease of look and manner. A very friendly inquiry after Miss Fairfax, she hoped, might lead the way to a return of old feelings.

   Volubility is NOT characterized by
   a. interaction
   b. silence
   c. expression
   d. verbalization

Interactive Quiz

Snap the code, or go to **vocabularyworkshop.com**

Vocabulary for Comprehension

*Read the following selection in which some of the words you have studied in Units 13–15 appear in **boldface** type. Then answer the questions on page 195.*

The subject of the following passage is Isaac Asimov, a popular and prolific twentieth-century science fiction writer.

(Line)

Isaac Asimov (1920–1992) has been **lauded** in many quarters as a master of the science fiction genre, and several of his books reached the
(5) best-seller lists. Unlike some other writers in the field, however, Asimov always **renounced** the view that science fiction should be pure fantasy. Instead, he championed
(10) what is sometimes called *hard* science fiction—science fiction that incorporates up-to-date scientific and technical facts and theories in order to seem as plausible as
(15) possible.

Asimov, who was also a scientist and an academic, was a **zealous** believer in the usefulness of science to humanity and of the rational
(20) approach to solving human problems. He expressed **chagrin** that humanity often seems unable and unwilling to learn the lessons that science and history have to
(25) teach. These beliefs are reflected in his science fiction. He wanted to make readers think about where society may be heading if present trends continue.
(30) Millions of readers are **receptive** to Asimov's ideas because of the context in which he presented them. Much of the appeal of his stories lies

in the inventiveness of the imaginary worlds he created. His extremely
(35) popular Foundation stories were written one at a time for the magazine *Astounding Science Fiction* in the 1940s; and in the early
(40) 1950s, they were collected and published in book form. These stories are among the finest examples of what has become a familiar science fiction motif: The rise
(45) and fall of a galactic empire. Asimov called his galactic empire Trantor. Though it was not a **facsimile** of any actual empire, its vast size and centralized administration call to
(50) mind imperial Rome. This is not surprising, since Asimov read Edward Gibbon's classic history of the Roman Empire twice before the age of twenty.
(55) Another outstanding element of Asimov's science fiction was the development of the robot as a concept and a character. Though he did not invent the idea, Asimov
(60) imaginatively extended the concept of robotics in his 1950 collection *I, Robot*. His premises came to be accepted by other science fiction writers and even by researchers into
(65) artificial intelligence.

1. The passage is best described as
   a. an explanation of the origin of robotics
   b. a criticism of the genre of science fiction
   c. an introduction to Isaac Asimov's Foundation stories
   d. a description of the life and times of Isaac Asimov
   e. an assessment of Isaac Asimov's contributions to science fiction

2. The meaning of **lauded** (line 2) is
   a. criticized
   b. extolled
   c. studied
   d. quoted
   e. listed

3. **Renounced** (line 7) most nearly means
   a. embraced
   b. proclaimed
   c. repudiated
   d. remembered
   e. acknowledged

4. Evidently Asimov was critical of
   a. imperial Rome
   b. artificial intelligence
   c. the genre of nonfiction
   d. nonscientific science fiction
   e. scientific progress

5. By championing hard science fiction, Asimov
   a. made science fiction more credible
   b. made science fiction less accessible
   c. invented science fiction
   d. made science fiction less popular
   e. renounced science fiction

6. **Zealous** (line 17) is best defined as
   a. superstitious
   b. halfhearted
   c. ardent
   d. generous
   e. fitful

7. The meaning of **chagrin** (line 21) is
   a. fear
   b. anger
   c. delight
   d. mortify
   e. disappointment

8. **Receptive** (line 30) most nearly means
   a. hostile
   b. related
   c. indifferent
   d. responsive
   e. addicted

9. **Facsimile** (line 47) is best defined as
   a. duplicate
   b. description
   c. variation
   d. analysis
   e. satire

10. Asimov's Foundation stories bring into play all of the following EXCEPT
    a. fantasy and horror
    b. a knowledge of history
    c. human problems
    d. a futuristic setting
    e. a knowledge of science

11. In the last paragraph (lines 55–65), the author cites robotics primarily as an example of Asimov's
    a. originality
    b. humanism
    c. imagination
    d. automation
    e. professionalism

12. The author's attitude toward Asimov is best described as
    a. critical
    b. irritating
    c. astounding
    d. laudatory
    e. challenging

Two-Word Completions

Select the pair of words that best complete the meaning of each of the following passages.

1. I might not be so _____ about suggesting improvements at the office if my boss were more _____ to constructive criticism. But since he seems to resent it, I keep such ideas to myself.
a. phlegmatic . . . implacable
b. zealous . . . magnanimous
c. reticent . . . receptive
d. exuberant . . . compassionate

2. Though it didn't rule out mild soap, the warranty expressly _____ that _____ cleansers should not be used on the floor because they would damage the tile surface.
a. stipulated . . . abrasive
b. explicated . . . innocuous
c. rescinded . . . applicable
d. concurred . . . dissonant

3. Edna's _____, offbeat sense of humor proved to be a considerable _____ in the competition for class wit.
a. nondescript . . . facsimile
b. grotesque . . . antithesis
c. savory . . . fracas
d. droll . . . asset

4. Though the supply of winter uniforms had done much to _____ the hardship suffered by the troops, the continuing shortage of ammunition and the ominous weather forecast _____ against pressing the attack.
a. beset . . . concurred
b. alleviate . . . militated
c. acclimate . . . stipulated
d. whet . . . elucidated

5. Alexander the Great was a(n) _____ foe of the Persians as long as they posed a threat to Greek security. But once he had conquered them, he proved to be a(n) _____ and fair ruler.
a. vehement . . . repressive
b. somnolent . . . innocuous
c. phlegmatic . . . nondescript
d. implacable . . . magnanimous

6. "Since the documents are only _____ of the Declaration of Independence," the salesperson said, "the price I'm asking for them is _____ in comparison with what the real thing would cost."
a. antitheses . . . grotesque
b. facsimiles . . . infinitesimal
c. patents . . . savory
d. edicts . . . voluble

7. Like a Roman emperor of old, the new principal issued a(n) _____ stating that attendance at morning assembly, which had been optional under the old regime, was now _____.
a. edict . . . mandatory
b. facsimile . . . applicable
c. patent . . . complacent
d. defamation . . . sedate

Proverbs

In "Life on the High Seas," the log of a sailor aboard the *Endeavour* (see pages 164–165), the sailor describes a celebration on land, using the expression "better poor on land than rich at sea"—a Danish proverb that comments on the fact that no wealth can compete with the freedom and comforts a sailor can enjoy on land after a long time of hardship at sea.

A **proverb** is a short saying that conveys a universal truth about life. Proverbs offer advice and wisdom—they are like minilessons. Many proverbs originate from the Bible, Shakespeare's plays, and epic literature, though many others are folk sayings that have simply been passed down by word of mouth. Proverbs use such devices as rhyme, figures of speech, and clever turns of phrase to make their memorable points.

Choosing the Right Proverb

Read each sentence. Use context clues to figure out the meaning of each proverb in **boldface** *print. Then write the letter of the definition for the proverb in the sentence.*

1. My neighbor frittered away thousands of dollars on useless products he didn't need, proving once again that **a fool and his money are soon parted**. _____

2. Those who know that **necessity is the mother of invention** can do a lot with few resources. _____

3. I had to remind myself that **little strokes fell great oaks** as I began my third week of training. _____

4. I know it bothered you when she refused to go to the movie, but **don't make a mountain out of a molehill**. _____

5. Deciding that a **rolling stone gathers no moss**, Ashley set out to find a new job. _____

6. After I scored the winning goal, I twisted my ankle badly, but I decided to **take the bitter with the sweet**. _____

7. Don't expect him to suddenly start being caring and helpful when you get out of the hospital; you know **you can't get blood from a stone**. _____

8. Ryan was at first disappointed that he had to share the prize money, but he quickly decided that **half a loaf is better than none**. _____

9. My coach berates us for the smallest mistake; I guess she never learned that **you can catch more flies with honey than with vinegar**. _____

10. Since **there's no time like the present**, I might as well start working on my report. _____

a. Don't exaggerate a small problem, turning it into a large one.

b. Accept life's misfortunes along with its pleasures.

c. Something is better than nothing.

d. Don't put things off; just do them now.

e. Those who are not wise about money will squander it.

f. If you are on the move you won't get stuck.

g. Persistence can help you succeed at a task that seems daunting.

h. People cannot give you what they do not have to give.

i. You will have more success by being kind than by being punitive.

j. Clever solutions can be prompted by difficult circumstances.

Writing with Proverbs

Find the meaning of each proverb. (Use an online or print dictionary if necessary.) Then write a sentence for each proverb.

1. One swallow does not a summer make.

_____

2. You can't judge a book by its cover.

_____

3. Nothing ventured, nothing gained.

_____

4. Brevity is the soul of wit.

_____

5. Forewarned is forearmed.

_____

_____

6. The pen is mightier than the sword.

_____

_____

7. Penny wise and pound foolish

_____

_____

8. A little knowledge is a dangerous thing.

_____

9. Good things come in small packages.

_____

10. Slow and steady wins the race.

_____

11. Out of the frying pan and into the fire

_____

12. It's better to light a candle than curse the darkness.

_____

Denotation and Connotation

Words have two kinds of meaning. The first meaning is the literal, *neutral* meaning of a word—its **denotation**, or dictionary definition. The second meaning of a word is the emotional association that is connected to it—its **connotation**, which may be *positive* or *negative*.

Suppose a student writer wants to describe how large her dog is. She can use the words *big*, *huge*, *enormous*, *gigantic*, *gargantuan*, *massive*, *colossal*, and so on. Each one of these words conveys a different association or image. A writer can create a vivid picture or a specific mood simply by choosing one word over another.

Consider these synonyms for the neutral word *implacable*:

unbending   *unyielding*   *relentless*   *obdurate*

Unbending and *unyielding* can suggest positive connotations, hinting at an inner strength that can stand firm in adversity. *Relentless* and *obdurate* have more negative connotations, suggesting severe, inflexible, hardhearted characteristics.

> **Think:** A hero can be unbending or unyielding while fighting an enemy, but that enemy may be relentless and obdurate as he mercilessly assaults the hero.

Look at these examples of words. Notice how the connotation of each word varies.

NEUTRAL	POSITIVE	NEGATIVE
satisfied	contented	complacent
amusing	droll	eccentric
palatable	savory	tolerable

Writers in any field must choose their words carefully. All restaurants sell food, but do they advertise *home-style cooking* or *haute cuisine?* Are the desserts *tasty* or *delectable*? Writers craft precise messages based on the emotional power of words.

Shades of Meaning

Write a plus sign (+) in the box if the word has a positive connotation. Write a minus sign (–) if the word has a negative connotation. Put a zero (0) if the word is neutral.

1. duress ☐   **2.** facsimile ☐   **3.** decorum ☐   **4.** exuberance ☐

5. elucidate ☐   **6.** nondescript ☐   **7.** concur ☐   **8.** patent ☐

9. magnanimous ☐   **10.** whet ☐   **11.** chagrin ☐   **12.** militate ☐

13. bellicose ☐   **14.** grotesque ☐   **15.** receptive ☐   **16.** alacrity ☐

Expressing the Connotation

Read each sentence. Select the word in parentheses that expresses the connotation (positive, negative, or neutral) given at the beginning of the sentence.

positive | **1.** We passed a large crowd of (**raucous, vivacious**) college students who were celebrating New Year's Eve.

neutral | **2.** I appreciate your (**compassion, concern**), but I would rather be alone during my time of grief.

negative | **3.** When someone in the crowd threw a shoe, a (**riot, fracas**) ensued and the police were called in.

negative | **4.** Due to Uncle Ron's (**abrasive, rough**) manners, he is seldom included in family gatherings.

positive | **5.** I sincerely hope that a cold compress will (**lessen, alleviate**) the pain in your back.

neutral | **6.** When the (**somnolent, lethargic**) bear had fully awakened from his slumber, he was hungry.

neutral | **7.** Many students and parents are opposed to (**required, mandatory**) locker searches in elementary school.

positive | **8.** A (**magnanimous, considerate**) coach will never disparage players' failed efforts but will instead offer support and constructive criticism.

Challenge: Using Connotation

Choose vocabulary words from Units 13–15 to replace the highlighted words in the sentences below. Then explain how the connotation of the replacement word changes the tone of the sentence.

ultimatum	phlegmatic	prowess
pandemonium	vehement	antithesis

1. The story begins with a **passionate** _____ argument between the queen and king.

_____

_____

2. The commander gave his adversaries a **final offer** _____—they could surrender immediately or face a long and agonizing battle.

_____

_____

3. Gabriela, known for her negotiating **skills** _____, was able to buy her new car for well under the sticker price.

_____

_____

Classical Roots

sed, sess, sid—to sit, settle

The root *sed* appears in **sedate** (page 168). The literal meaning is "settled," but the word now means "quiet or calm." Some other words based on the same root are listed below.

assess	**obsessed**	**sediment**	**subsidiary**
dissidence	**residual**	**subside**	**supersede**

From the list of words above, choose the one that corresponds to each of the brief definitions below. Write the word in the blank space in the illustrative sentence below the definition. Use an online or print dictionary if necessary.

1. to estimate the value of; to fix an amount, tax; to determine the importance, value, or size of

A gym or health club may _____ new members a fee at the time they join.

2. disagreement in opinion or belief; dissent

The nominating convention was disrupted by noisy _____.

3. excessively troubled or preoccupied by

A person who is _____ with the details of a project may have trouble seeing the "big picture."

4. remaining; left over

After I pay my monthly bills, I deposit some of the _____ money in my savings account.

5. matter that settles to the bottom of a liquid; lees, dregs

Catfish and snails will help to keep your aquarium free of _____.

6. to displace in favor of another; replace; force out of use

In many homes, streaming video has _____ DVDs, just as music downloads have replaced CDs.

7. furnishing aid or support; of secondary importance; a thing or person that assists or supplements

Evening newscasts generally cover major stories but don't have time to examine _____ issues.

8. to grow less; become less active; to die down (*"to settle down"*)

The candidate could not begin to speak until the uproar _____.

Synonyms

Select the two words or expressions that are most nearly the same in meaning.

1. **a.** threatening **b.** ominous **c.** applicable **d.** unexplained
2. **a.** emaciated **b.** shy **c.** rude **d.** diffident
3. **a.** unfeigned **b.** contentious **c.** sincere **d.** hypocritical
4. **a.** asset **b.** courage **c.** fortitude **d.** intelligence
5. **a.** spiteful **b.** copious **c.** indifferent **d.** malevolent
6. **a.** worried **b.** elated **c.** apprehensive **d.** unreasonable
7. **a.** early **b.** inopportune **c.** inconvenient **d.** pleasant
8. **a.** duplicity **b.** pinnacle **c.** stubbornness **d.** deceitfulness
9. **a.** complacent **b.** bellicose **c.** quarrelsome **d.** phlegmatic
10. **a.** healthful **b.** exacting **c.** squalid **d.** wretched
11. **a.** misinterpret **b.** dangerous **.c.** misconstrue **d.** rampant
12. **a.** accustomed **b.** opposed **c.** averse **d.** untrained
13. **a.** study **b.** ponder **c.** relax **.d.** ruminate
14. **a.** luxurious **b.** opulent **c.** culinary **d.** poverty-stricken
15. **a.** vociferous **b.** subtle **c.** noisy **d.** pliable

Antonyms

Select the two words that are most nearly opposite in meaning.

16. **a.** obey **b.** antagonize **c.** placate **d.** remain
17. **a.** intellectual **b.** petty **c.** magnanimous **d.** disturbed
18. **a.** incite **b.** organize **c.** train **d.** quell
19. **a.** youthful **b.** expected **c.** dour **d.** amicable
20. **a.** loquacious **b.** infinitesimal **c.** colossal **d.** profitable
21. **a.** deny **b.** embezzle **c.** clarify **d.** profess
22. **a.** foreign **b.** virulent **c.** harmless **d.** charming
23. **a.** scrupulous **b.** glorious **c.** natural **d.** cursory
24. **a.** palatable **b.** dangerous **c.** disagreeable **d.** foolish
25. **a.** fathom **b.** militate **c.** support **d.** sacrifice

Analogies

Select the item that best completes the comparison.

26. pauper is to **destitute** as
a. peacemaker is to truculent
b. benefactor is to altruistic
c. bigot is to chivalrous
d. klutz is to deft

27. eraser is to **expunge** as
a. ice is to liquidate
b. rake is to elucidate
c. scalpel is to extirpate
d. sieve is to comprise

28. insidious is to **entrap** as
a. zealous is to trick
b. meticulous is to alienate
c. benevolent is to harass
d. punitive is to punishment

29. infirm is to **decrepit** as
a. sorrow is to reparation
b. frugal is to parsimonious
c. scanty is to copious
d. indifferent is to ardent

30. abhor is to **palatable** as
a. deride is to voluminous
b. inter is to deviate
c. commend is to reprehensible
d. consecrate is to spontaneous

31. cursory is to **haste** as
a. tepid is to ardor
b. infinitesimal is to large
c. urbane is to awkwardness
d. tentative is to hesitation

32. irrelevant is to **applicability** as
a. clairvoyant is to discernment
b. superficial is to depth
c. contentious is to aggressiveness
d. exemplary is to praiseworthy

33. assiduous is to **persistence** as
a. sonorous is to grating
b. omnipotent is to envy
c. voluble is to boredom
d. recalcitrant is to stubbornness

Two-Word Completions

Select the best word pair from among the choices given.

34. Although the enemy army was exhausted, it remained as _____ as ever; still, it did not stand a chance against the brave soldiers who felt _____ on the battlefield.
a. nonchalant . . . rampant
b. tepid . . . tentative
c. implacable . . . invulnerable
d. destitute . . . venial

35. It is not wise to _____ another person, because one day, you may regret your _____ words.
a. perpetuate . . . turbulent
b. renounce . . . sophomoric
c. coerce . . . malevolent
d. disparage . . . corrosive

36. People decried the clerk's _____ manner and attributed it to his mistaken belief that he was _____.
a. officious . . . omnipotent
b. musty . . . droll
c. reticent . . . diffident
d. vehement . . . loquacious

37. It is _____ that when some people become famous and successful, they become arrogant and _____ to criticism.
a. lamentable . . . impervious
b. venal . . . inclement
c. indomitable. . . nonchalant
d. endemic . . . pliable

Supplying Words in Context

To complete each sentence, select the best word from among the choices given. Not all words in the word bank will be used. You may modify the word form as necessary.

stultify	dissonant	esteem	suave
solace	consecrate	conclusive	trenchant
gibe	sedate	vivacious	suppress
temerity	guile	warily	somber

38. The fingerprints were regarded as _____ evidence of his guilt.

39. Her _____ remarks cut right to the heart of the issue under discussion.

40. Let's ignore their vicious _____ and do what we think is right.

41. He is so _____ that he seems to fit into any social situation without the slightest difficulty.

42. The view from his window of the dismal winter landscape put him in a very _____ mood.

43. Despite his fear-mongering and strict laws, the dictator was unable to _____ the spirit of freedom.

adversary	ironic	implicate	compatible
gnarled	inveterate	condolence	dearth
multifarious	tacit	finite	garrulous
misnomer	facsimile	feasible	redress

44. As a(n) _____ concertgoer, my friend Sandra has seen many great musicians perform.

45. With all her _____ activities, it's a wonder she finds time to sleep.

46. It would be a(n) _____ to nickname that crook "Honest John."

47. Not a word was said, but we had a(n) _____ understanding between us of the plan.

48. I'll have to be at my best on the tennis court to beat a formidable _____ such as Ken.

49. The plan was deemed not _____, since we did not have sufficient funds.

Word Associations

*Select the word or expression that best completes the meaning of the sentence or answers the question, with particular reference to the meaning of the word in **boldface** type.*

50. You would **extol** something that you find
- **a.** contentious
- **b.** commendable
- **c.** innocuous
- **d.** crestfallen

51. A nation that is a **belligerent** is engaged in
- **a.** war
- **b.** industrialization
- **c.** land reform
- **d.** energy conservation

52. To **skulk** out of a room suggests
- **a.** haste
- **b.** happiness
- **c.** sneakiness
- **d.** listlessness

53. Which nickname would a **craven** person be most likely to have?
- **a.** Alibi Ike
- **b.** Chicken Little
- **c.** Fancy Dan
- **d.** Calamity Jane

54. You would be most likely to read of **uncanny** events in
- **a.** a history textbook
- **b.** a detective story
- **c.** a novel of social protest
- **d.** a ghost story

55. Which of the following suggests that a team is being **derided**?
- **a.** "We're number one!"
- **b.** "Go get 'em!"
- **c.** "You guys are losers!"
- **d.** "Give us a break, umpire!"

56. A movie that is exceptionally **poignant** is likely to
- **a.** put you to sleep
- **b.** touch your emotions
- **c.** get a lot of laughs
- **d.** fail at the box office

57. The word **demise** suggests that someone or something has
- **a.** won a prize
- **b.** failed an examination
- **c.** passed out of existence
- **d.** gained final approval

58. To be **somnolent** implies a desire to
- **a.** eat
- **b.** exercise
- **c.** get out of town
- **d.** sleep

59. We may apply the word **stately** to
- **a.** a duchess and a sailing ship
- **b.** a robot and a computer
- **c.** a city and a state
- **d.** a gibe and a grimace

60. A picture that is **askew** should be
- **a.** dusted
- **b.** given a price
- **c.** straightened
- **d.** sold to the highest bidder

61. If people refer to Darryl as **obnoxious**, he should try to
- **a.** speak more clearly
- **b.** behave more agreeably
- **c.** smile more often
- **d.** learn to play soccer

Choosing the Right Meaning

Read each sentence carefully. Then select the item that best completes the statement below the sentence.

62. I didn't realize how **disheveled** I looked after basketball practice until my mother looked at me and said, "Look what the cat dragged in."

The word **disheveled** most nearly means

a. unkempt **b.** tired **c.** defeated **d.** victorious

63. In the chapter on Benedict Arnold in my history book, the author referred to him as a **renegade**.

The word **renegade** most nearly means

a. heretic **b.** patriot **c.** martyr **d.** soldier

64. I purchased this copy of Dickens's *A Tale of Two Cities* at the bookstore because the price was as **negligible** there as it was online.

The word **negligible** most nearly means

a. expensive **b.** equal **c.** inconsequential **d.** significant

65. Doctors prescribed a new medicine in the hope it would **obviate** the effects of the highly contagious virus.

The word **obviate** most nearly means

a. augment **b.** repair **c.** allocate **d.** remove

66. Prince Hal, the main character in Shakespeare's play *Henry IV*, is often called a fun-loving **wastrel**.

The word **wastrel** most nearly means

a. childish **b.** naughty **c.** good-for-nothing **d.** miser

67. Marla suggests that we study before going to the game, and I **concur** with that practical plan.

The best definition for the word **concur** is

a. differ **b.** agree **c.** disagree **d.** regret

68. The lawyers argued over a **discrepancy** between what the accused said had happened and what the witness said she saw.

The word **discrepancy** most nearly means

a. convergence **b.** argument **c.** inconsistency **d.** accusation

69. The sports commentator is as **facile** with words as she was on the playing field.

The word **facile** most nearly means

a. pleasant **b.** assured **c.** awkward **d.** unbeatable

70. I keep a map in my pocket even though my father claims he has an **infallible** sense of direction.

The word **infallible** is best defined as

a. memorable **b.** ingenuous **c.** unerring **d.** imperfect

WORD LIST

The following is a list of all the words taught in the Units of this book. The number after each entry indicates the page on which the word is defined.

abhor, 90
abjure, 148
abrasive, 186
accede, 72
acclimate, 186
acquiesce, 128
acrid, 148
adroit, 24
adulterate, 14
adversary, 34
affiliated, 52
alacrity, 176
alienate, 34
alleviate, 176
allocate, 110
allude, 138
allure, 128
altruistic, 62
ambidextrous, 14
amend, 90
amicable, 24
animosity, 100
antipathy, 166
antithesis, 176
apathy, 100
appall, 176
applicable, 166
apprehensive, 100
ardent, 110
artifice, 34
ascertain, 52
askew, 128
assent, 62
asset, 166
assiduous, 110
attainment, 52
augment, 14
august, 148
averse, 24

bellicose, 176
belligerent, 24
benefactor, 62
benevolent, 24
bequeath, 52
bereft, 14
beset, 166
blithe, 128

brandish, 72
brash, 110
buffet, 90

callous, 148
capricious, 110
chagrin, 186
chaos, 90
chastise, 110
chivalrous, 62
clairvoyant, 138
clandestine, 148
clemency, 62
coerce, 34
cogent, 52
commend, 100
commodious, 90
compassion, 166
compatible, 100
complacent, 186
comprise, 72
compunction, 148
conclusive, 138
concur, 186
condolence, 100
conflagration, 149
consecrate, 101
contentious, 128
converge, 52
copious, 111
corrosive, 90
covet, 129
craven, 34
crestfallen, 129
culinary, 34
cursory, 24

dearth, 62
decorum, 166
decrepit, 101
defamation, 186
deft, 72
demise, 35
deploy, 14
deride, 101
destitute, 72
deviate, 111
diffident, 63

discern, 91
discrepancy, 63
disheveled, 129
disparage, 176
disperse, 53
disreputable, 138
dissonant, 176
dour, 14
droll, 177
duplicity, 25
duress, 167

edict, 177
elated, 149
elucidate, 177
emaciated, 111
embark, 63
endemic, 138
esteem, 53
exemplary, 138
exhilarate, 35
explicate, 187
explicit, 72
exponent, 129
expunge, 53
extant, 91
extirpate, 73
extol, 25
exuberant, 167
exult, 111

facile, 63
facsimile, 167
fallow, 35
fathom, 139
feasible, 25
finite, 53
fortitude, 15
fracas, 187

gape, 15
garrulous, 129
gibe, 15
gnarled, 111
grimace, 25
grotesque, 187
guile, 139
guise, 15

harass, 35
holocaust, 25

imbibe, 167
impervious, 25
impetus, 25
implacable, 167
implicate, 91
inclement, 35
indelible, 149
indemnity, 111
indomitable, 63
indulgent, 149
infallible, 63
infinitesimal, 167
ingenuous, 101
inkling, 112
innocuous, 167
inopportune, 73
insidious, 15
insuperable, 129
integrity, 139
inter, 91
intimation, 15
inveterate, 149
invulnerable, 53
ironic, 73
irrelevant, 149
itinerary, 139

jeopardy, 26

lamentable, 129
laud, 177
limpid, 112
liquidate, 35
loll, 177
loquacious, 177

magnanimous, 177
malevolent, 53
mandatory, 178
martinet, 91
meticulous, 26
militate, 167
misconstrue, 139
misnomer, 130
multifarious, 101

INDEX